MARY

A Biblical Walk with the Blessed Mother

STUDY SET

EDWARD SRI

ASCENSION PRESS

West Chester, Pennsylvania

Nihil obstat: Rev. Msgr. J. Brian Bransfield, S.T.D.
                 Censor Librorum
                 January 24, 2014

Imprimatur: +Most Reverend Charles J. Chaput, O.F.M. Cap.
                 Archbishop of Philadelphia
                 January 31, 2014

Mary: A Biblical Walk with the Blessed Mother is a resource of *The Great Adventure* Catholic Bible Study Program.

Edward Sri, Author and Presenter, *Mary: A Biblical Walk with the Blessed Mother*

Jeff Cavins, General Editor, *The Great Adventure* Catholic Bible Study Program

Sarah Christmyer, Editor, *The Great Adventure* Catholic Bible Study Program

Ascension Press
Post Office Box 1990
West Chester, PA 19380
1-800-376-0520
AscensionPress.com
BibleStudyForCatholics.com

Printed in the United States of America

ISBN 978-1-935940-75-3

Cover design: Devin Schadt

MARY

A Biblical Walk with the Blessed Mother

Contents

Welcome to *The Great Adventure*

*"To fall in love with God is the greatest of all romances;
to seek him, the greatest adventure."*

– St. Augustine

The Bible is at the heart of our Catholic Faith—and our relationship with God. It is the living Word of God, where our Father meets with us and lovingly speaks to us. Reading the Bible should bring us closer to Christ, but understanding it is not always easy. Many people tell us they have tried time and again to prayfully read Scripture, but they get frustrated because they "just don't get it."

The Great Adventure is designed so that anyone can make sense of the Bible and experience the life-changing power of God's Word. At the core of *The Great Adventure* is the concept that there is a story running through the seventy-three books of the Bible that ties all of Scripture together and makes sense not just of the Bible, but of our lives as well.

That story is God's plan as it has unfolded throughout salvation history and continues to unfold today. Once we grasp this "big picture," the readings at Mass begin to make more sense, our Scripture reading and study come to life, and we see how our lives fit into God's loving plan.

Hundreds of thousands of participants have discovered the riches of Scripture by experiencing one or more *Great Adventure* Bible studies. It is our prayer that you will gain a newfound understanding of God's Word that will transform your life and bring you closer to Christ.

Jeff Cavins, Creator & President, *The Great Adventure*
Sarah Christmyer, Co-developer & Author, *The Great Adventure*

About *The Great Adventure* Catholic Bible Study Program

At the core of *The Great Adventure* is *The Bible Timeline* Learning System: a simple way to get the "big picture" of the Bible by focusing on the story that runs throughout Sacred Scripture. *Great Adventure* Bible studies explore the biblical narrative in light of Catholic teaching and the historical, cultural, and literary context of the Scriptures to discover what Scripture reveals about God's plan and our place within it. Studies of individual books of the Bible are supplemented by thematic and "life application" studies.

Every *Great Adventure* study is designed to foster:

- Familiarity with the Bible and ease of reading it

- Bible study habits consistent with the guidelines of the Catholic Church

- Personal engagement in the Word of God

- Faith-sharing based on the Word of God

- Growth in knowledge about Scripture and the Catholic Faith

About *Mary: A Biblical Walk with the Blessed Mother*

Mary: A Biblical Walk with the Blessed Mother is a powerful Bible study that reveals Mary's unique role in God's kingdom and in our lives. You will experience the gospel through the eyes of Mary and get a vivid glimpse into her daily life. Seeing her in this way will lead you to a deeper relationship with the Blessed Mother and her son, Jesus.

The following timeline of Mary's life appears on the first page of each session with the portion related to that session emphasized.

Materials

Materials for *Mary: A Biblical Walk with the Blessed Mother* include:

- **The Study Set** – Contains engaging study questions (with session summaries, home reading assignments, talk notes, charts, and diagrams), and responses to the questions. *(You will need one Study Set for every participant, study leader, and small-group facilitator.)*

- **Video Presentations** (eight, 30-minute sessions) – Presented by Dr. Edward Sri, these eight video presentations paint an amazing picture of Mary and provide you with a uniquely personal encounter with the Blessed Mother. *(You will need one DVD Set.)*

- *The Great Adventure* **Bible Study Leader's Companion** (free download) provides step-by-step instructions for leaders on planning, promoting, running, and facilitating a Bible study. *(This Leader's Companion is available at BibleStudyForCatholics.com/downloads.)*

In addition, every participant, leader, and small-group facilitator should have a Catholic Bible. We recommend the Revised Standard Version–Catholic Edition (RSV-CE) or the New American Bible (NAB).

How the Study Works

Every *Great Adventure* study session includes four essential steps, which are designed to fit together and build upon each other. Following these steps in order will allow you to get the most out of each session.

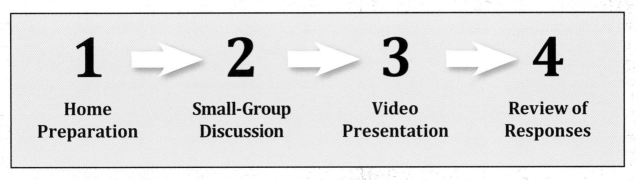

Step 1: Home Preparation

Note: There is no home preparation required for Session One.

Each session begins with personal study that involves reading Scripture and answering a series of questions that will help you understand and think more deeply about what you have read. Some questions will include additional reading from other parts of the Bible or from the *Catechism of the Catholic Church* to help you consider the passage in light of the bigger picture of salvation history and Catholic teaching.

We recommend that you allow at least 90 minutes to complete the reading and answer the questions for each session. We also suggest that home preparation be done in several sittings over the course of a week. This will help you create a habit of daily Bible reading and prayerful meditation.

Step 2: Small-Group Discussion

One of the richest parts of a *Great Adventure* Bible study is the small-group discussion. During this discussion, you and the other members of your small group will have the opportunity to share your insights into the Scripture readings. This small-group discussion will allow you to obtain a richer understanding of these readings and help you apply them to your life. Trained facilitators will guide the small-group discussions and keep them on track. Be sure to follow the "Ten Commandments of Small-Group-Discussion" on page viii.

Step: 3: Video Presentation

Dr. Edward Sri wraps up each session with a video presentation that offers unique insights and profound connections to help you gain a deeper understanding of the Bible and its relationship to the Catholic Faith, with a special emphasis on ways to apply what you have learned to your life.

Step 4: Review of Responses

Note: There are no responses for Session One.

The final step—reviewing the responses at the back of this Study Set—is done at home prior to beginning the reading for the next session. These responses will help you read the Scripture passages for the next session in the proper context.

For the richest study experience, complete these steps in order: (1) Read and answer the questions; (2) discuss them in your small group; (3) view the video presentation; and (4) review the responses. Your small-group facilitator will incorporate the points made in the responses section during your discussion time, but the richness that comes from individual insights can be lost when participants view the responses prior to the discussion.

For more information about how to plan and promote a Bible study and how to facilitate a small-group discussion, visit **BibleStudyForCatholics.com/leaders,** or call our Study Consultants at 1-800-376-0520.

Session Outline and Reading Guide

Each session in this Study Set has the following sections. *(Note: The Introduction follows a different format.)*

1. **Session Questions** (used during **Step 1: Home Preparation** and **Step 2: Small-Group Discussion**)

   A. Establish (or Review) the Context

   B. Read the Story

   C. Take a Deeper Look

   D. Application

2. **Session Talk Notes** (used during **Step 3: Video Presentation**)

3. **Session Responses** (used during **Step 4: Review of Responses**)

The following chart offers an overview of the **home preparation** readings assigned in each session of the study. The main reading is provided in section **B. Read the Story** and should be read before you answer the session questions. Additional Bible readings and Catechism readings are provided in section **C. Take a Deeper Look** and should be read as you answer the study questions for each session.

Session	Main Reading	Additional Bible Readings	*Catechism* Readings (CCC)
1. Introduction (20:15)	(None)	(None)	(None)
2. The Annunciation (24:17)	Luke 1:26-38	Exodus 3:10-12; Judges 6:14-18; 2 Samuel 7:9-16; Zephaniah 3:14-15; Zechariah 9:9; Matthew 6:10; Luke 22:42	485, 723
3. The Visitation (27:28)	Luke 1:39-56	Judges 5:24-26; 2 Samuel 6:2, 9-16; 24:21; 1 Kings 2:19-20; 2 Kings 24:12; Judith 13:18; Proverbs 31:1-12; Luke 1:1-25	2676–2677
4. The Nativity (22:36)	Luke 2:1-20	Genesis 37:5-11; Psalm 119:11; Proverbs 3:1-2; Micah 5:2-4 (NAB 5:1-3); Luke 23:53	563, 725

Continued on next page

Continued from previous page

Session	Main Reading	Additional Bible Readings	*Catechism* Readings (CCC)
5. The Presentation & The Finding of Jesus in the Temple (28:16)	Luke 2:21-52	Leviticus 12:8; 26:6-7; Deuteronomy 32:25; Isaiah 42:1-6; Luke 9:22, 51; 19:45; 22:1; John 19:31-35	529, 534
6. The Wedding at Cana (29:45)	John 2:1-11	Exodus 3:14-15; 19:8; Joshua 24:24; Nehemiah 5:12; John 1; 20:29	410–411
7. Mary at the Cross (37:34)	John 19:25-30	Genesis 3:15; 2 Maccabees 7:1-39; Matthew 16:21, 24, 32; 26:56; John 5:25-28; 7:30; 12:23-24, 27, 31-33; 13:25; 16:20-22; 20:8; 21:7	501, 2618, 2674
8. Mary Crowned with Glory (29:31)	Revelation 12:1-17	Genesis 3:15; Psalm 2:9; Luke 1:38-39; 45; 2:19, 51; John 19:25-27; Acts 1:14; 2 Timothy 4:7-8	501

What to Do for Each Session

1. Welcome and Introduction (10 minutes)

2. Small-Group Discussion (40 minutes)
   Note to Study Leaders: There is no small-group discussion for the first week. Instead, use this time to divide participants into small groups of eight to twelve people, ensure that everyone has the study materials, and explain how the study works. Each small group should be led by a trained facilitator.

3. Video Presentation (25-30 minutes)

4. Closing and Prayer (5 minutes)

Getting the Most Out of This Study

This study will help you understand the Bible and the Blessed Mother in a new way. The "head knowledge" you gain will help you grow in "heart knowledge" as you follow up on what you have learned. The Bible will always remain a mystery, though, and that is part of the beauty of it: We can never exhaust the treasures of Scripture. Fortunately for us, the Bible is not a subject to master; it is a place to encounter the living Word of God.

Whenever you open your Bible to read, *start with prayer,* and place yourself in God's presence. You might take Samuel's prayer as your own: "Speak, LORD, for your servant is listening" (1 Samuel 3:10). When you read, adopt an attitude of listening. Try not to treat Scripture as a text, but as a personal message from God. What is he saying? What does it mean? And what does it mean for my life? If you come to the Word focused on having an encounter with the Lord, he will speak to your heart, and you will be transformed.

An Important Note About the Responses to the Study Questions

Responses to the study questions are provided in the back of this Study Set. These responses do not exhaust the meaning that can be found in the Scripture reading. People will have unique insights. The responses have two important functions:

1. They provide participants with a review of each session, which will help establish a context for the reading and questions in the following session. The best time to read the responses is just before starting on the next session.

2. The second purpose of the responses is to provide guidelines for the small-group facilitators. **Facilitators:** Complete the Scripture reading and answer the questions on your own before reading the responses in preparation for facilitating the small-group discussion.

Participants should not review the responses for each session until after the session is completed. Although it might be tempting to look at these responses in advance, it is important to wait for the following reasons.

1. Bible study is not about simply watching a video presentation or reading a Bible commentary. It is just as important to immerse yourself in the Word of God itself and engage it with your heart and mind. The questions in *The Great Adventure* studies are designed to draw you into the Scriptures so that the Word of God will be planted and grow in your heart. Reading a response written by someone else may satisfy your mind for a moment, but it will not result in the kind of growth that will occur if you attempt to answer the question on your own first.

2. The success of a small group depends on a good discussion. A group of participants who have spent time pondering the Scripture passages on their own will have more varied insights to discuss.

For these reasons, please wait to read the responses until after the session. When you follow the steps of this study as intended, you will explore the Word of God in different ways: in the reading, the small-group discussion, the video presentation, and, finally, in the responses. Follow these steps over time and you will be more than fed; you will learn to feed yourself.

Ten Commandments
of Small-Group Discussion

1. Enjoy yourself!

2. Speak with respect and charity.

3. Do not ridicule or dismiss what others say. Keep comments positive.

4. Come prepared.

5. If you were not able to prepare, let others speak first.

6. Stick to the topic and questions at hand.

7. Start and end on time.

8. Allow silence. Give people a chance to think.

9. Listen to others without interrupting.

10. Keep personal matters within the group.

Session One

Introduction

Annunciation · Visitation · Nativity · Presentation & Finding · Wedding · At the Cross · Crowning

"Behold, I am the handmaid of the Lord ..."

Mary: A Biblical Walk with the Blessed Mother

Many Christians revere Mary, the mother of Jesus, as the most important woman in salvation history. Catholics in particular hold Mary in high esteem. We often decorate our churches with statues, stained glass windows, and paintings of Mary. We recite prayers such as the Hail Mary and the Rosary in which we ask Mary to pray for us. We sing hymns that honor her and recognize special feast days related to aspects of Mary's life. The Catholic Church also teaches doctrines related to the Blessed Virgin Mary: She is the Mother of God; she was conceived without sin; she remained a virgin throughout her life; she was assumed body and soul into heaven.

Whatever our level of familiarity with Catholic Marian doctrine and devotion, one question we can ask ourselves is this: How well do we know the humanness of Mary and her profound journey of faith? How well do we know the young woman of Nazareth who was called to a most extraordinary mission and was led by God step-by-step into deeper trust and surrender to his plan and her son's mission?

The Bible does not offer a lot of information about Mary. She only appears in a few chapters in the New Testament. But these passages are packed with rich meaning and serve as important windows into Mary's life—and it is a life to which we can all relate and which offers much insight for our own journey of faith. We will see that Mary experienced the joys of motherhood and God's blessings, but that she also faced trials and sufferings. She had moments when God's will was clear to her and other moments of discernment, moments of darkness, and moments when she did not understand—when all she could do was keep all these things and ponder them in her heart. Mary certainly received extraordinary revelations, but not everything was disclosed to her at once. Though she was endowed with unique graces and privileges, she still had to walk by faith, not by sight.

In this study, we will walk with Mary through the stages of her life, starting with the angel Gabriel's announcement to her in Nazareth that she would become the mother of Jesus. We will accompany Mary on her visit to her kinswoman Elizabeth and consider what Mary was going through in the events surrounding her delivery of the child Jesus in Bethlehem; her presentation of the infant child in the Temple; and her losing and finding her child in Jerusalem when he was twelve years old.

We then will move ahead to study Mary's relationship with Jesus in his adult life. We will reflect on her role in the miracle at the wedding feast at Cana at the start of his public ministry and her role at the climax of his mission when he offered his life on the Cross. Finally, we will consider what the mysterious passage about "a woman clothed with the sun" in Revelation 12 may tell us about Mary's role in the life of the Christian today.

As we walk with Mary through her life, we will consider what the Bible tells us about her journey of faith, the practical lessons we can gain from her for our own relationship with God, and what the Scriptures tell us about Catholic Marian beliefs. We will focus on Mary in the Scriptures and on insights from Catholic Tradition that can help illuminate Mary's life.

It is my hope that this study will help you to know and love Mary more and to walk in her footsteps, imitating her as the first and model disciple of Christ.

Edward Sri

Session One *Talk Notes*

Introduction

I. Scope and Purpose: Getting to Know Mary as Revealed in Scripture

   A. Mary as model disciple

   B. Mary's journey of faith, from Nazareth to the Cross

   C. Inspiration and model for our lives

II. Facts About Mary's Early Life (Luke 1:26-27)

   A. Mary is from Nazareth

   1. Obscure town of two hundred people; in Galilee

   B. She is a virgin who is "betrothed"

   1. Two-step ancient Jewish marriage process

      a. First step: betrothal – legally bound, not living together

      b. Second step: taking into home of husband

    2. Typical age of girl at betrothal: thirteen or fourteen years old; a virgin

  C. Joseph is from the house of David (verse 27), the "royal family"

    1. 586 BC: end of Davidic dynasty

    2. Source of hope to the reader

      a. Messiah to come from house of David

      b. Joseph: from lineage of David

III. Role of Home Preparation

  A. Reading and study questions

  B. Join Mary – keep the Word in your heart

Basilica of the Annunciation, Nazareth

Session Two

The Annunciation

Luke 1:26-38

Annunciation · Visitation · Nativity · Presentation & Finding · Wedding · At the Cross · Crowning

" ... and the virgin's name was Mary."

A. Establish the Context

In Session One, we saw that the Bible does not tell us much about Mary's life before the angel Gabriel appears to her. We considered four facts that Luke's Gospel reveals about Mary's life before the Annunciation. First, she is from the obscure, insignificant village of Nazareth in Galilee. Second, she is betrothed, meaning that she is at the first stage of a two-step marriage process. Mary is legally married at this point, but she has not arrived at the stage when the bride would begin living with her husband and a marriage would normally be consummated. Third, Luke describes Mary as a virgin—which is what one would expect for a betrothed woman. And finally, Mary is betrothed to a man named Joseph who is from the house of David—the royal family line from which the Messiah is expected to come.

The Annunciation, by Bartolome Esteban Murillo

Now, we turn our attention to the angel Gabriel's announcement (*annunciation* means "announcement") to Mary that she will be the mother of Jesus. Put yourself in Mary's shoes and consider what the angel Gabriel's opening words—"Hail, full of grace, the Lord is with you"—mean to her and why she responds by being "greatly troubled." Next, we explore the angel's gradual revelation of Mary's mission. He tells her she is to become the mother of Israel's long-awaited Messiah—the King who will free the Jews from their enemies and establish a never-ending kingdom for Israel. She is also told that she will conceive this child as a virgin and that her son will be the Son of God. Finally, we ponder what Mary's reference to herself as "the handmaid of the Lord" and her consent to the will of God tell us about her relationship with God.

Archangel Gabriel Annunciate, by Fra Angelico

The Archangel Gabriel

Gabriel is Hebrew for "strong man of God" or "God is my strength." What does the angel Gabriel look like? Perhaps he resembles the angelic messenger in Daniel: "A man clothed in linen, whose loins were girded with gold of Uphaz. His body was like beryl, his face like the appearance of lightning, his eyes like flaming torches, his arms and legs like the gleam of burnished bronze, and the sound of his words like the noise of a multitude" (Daniel 10:5-6, NAB).

Along with Michael and Raphael, Gabriel is one of three archangels named in the Bible. We last saw Gabriel announcing to Daniel that "seventy weeks of years" (490 years) would remain after the Babylonian exile until the coming of the Messiah. And now, roughly five hundred years after the return of God's people to the Promised Land, he appears again. "I was sent ... to bring you this good news," he tells Zechariah as he announces the birth of John the Baptist (Luke 1:19). "Behold, you will conceive in your womb and bear a son," he tells Mary (Luke 1:31). The time of the long-awaited Messiah is at hand.

B. Read the Story

Read **Luke 1:26-38**, which gives the account of the angel's visit to Mary and his announcement to this young virgin from Nazareth.

C. Take a Deeper Look

Answering the following questions will help you understand the unique call Mary is given and her exemplary response of faith.

The Angel's Greeting (Luke 1:28)

From the moment Gabriel first speaks to Mary, it is clear there is something unique, not only about the child he will announce, but also about the mother. "Hail, full of grace," he begins—indicating that the grace of God has filled her, specially preparing her for the role she will play in his plan. Over time, the Church has grown in awareness of the truth underlying this "fullness of grace"—that Mary was redeemed and preserved free from original sin from the moment of her conception.[2]

1. Read **Luke 1:28.** The angel's first word to Mary, "Hail" (Gk., *chaire*), literally means "rejoice." The command to rejoice evokes several notable occasions in the Old Testament, where it is used to address "Daughter Zion"—a biblical symbol for the faithful remnant of God's people.

   a. Consider the following prophecies, and record the reasons God's people will one day be called to "rejoice."

      Zephaniah 3:14-15:

      Zechariah 9:9:

   b. In light of this background, what do you think Gabriel's command to rejoice signals to Mary?

> ### "Full of Grace": Mary's Immaculate Conception
>
> "Through the centuries the Church has become ever more aware that Mary, 'full of grace' through God (Luke 1:28), was redeemed from the moment of her conception. That is what the dogma of the Immaculate Conception confesses, as Pope Pius IX proclaimed in 1854:
>
> "'The most Blessed Virgin Mary was, from the first moment of her conception, by a singular grace and privilege of almighty God and by virtue of the merits of Jesus Christ, Savior of the human race, preserved immune from all stain of original sin.'"[1]
>
> [1] CCC 491; Pius IX, *Ineffabilis Deus*, 1854: DS 2803.

---

2. Mary is not the first person to hear the assurance that, "The Lord is with you." This expression is frequently used by God (and his angels) to address someone who is called to an important mission.

[2] CCC 490–491, 722.

a. Read the following verses about the call of two Old Testament heroes, Moses and Gideon. Record the missions they are given, the obstacles or fears they face, and what God says in response. Then do the same for the verses related to Mary.

Biblical Character	Mission	Obstacle/Fear	God's Assurance
Moses (Exodus 3:10-12)	Go to King - lead People out of Egypt	He was a nobody	He would be with him worship on the Mountain
Gideon (Judges 6:14-18)	Rescue Israel from Midianites	His clan was the weakest	The lord would help him crush
Mary (Luke 1:28-38)	Pregnant ā son of God	She is a Virgin	Holy Spirit Elizabeth

Eve & Mary

b. What similarities do you notice between these three scenes?
No heros — impossible situations —

c. Given the way the assurance that "the Lord will be with you" is used by God and his angels in the Old Testament, what do you think Gabriel's words, "The Lord is with you," are meant to indicate to Mary even before the message is given?

Mary's Initial Response (Luke 1:29)

3. Read **Luke 1:29.** On hearing the angel's greeting, Luke tells us that Mary is "greatly troubled." Why do you think she responds this way? Angels a common occurance? Confused by his words

The Mission Revealed (Luke 1:30-37)

Mary may have good reason to be troubled, but the angel reassures her in verse 30 that there is no need to fear, for she has "found favor with God": "The Father blessed Mary more than any other created person 'in Christ with every spiritual blessing in the heavenly places' and chose her 'in Christ before the foundation of the world, to be holy and blameless before him in love'" (CCC 492).[3]

---

[3] Cf. Ephesians 1:3-4.

4. The angel reveals Mary's mission in verse 31: "You will conceive in your womb and bear a son, and you shall call his name Jesus." Mary is to become a mother. But as the angel continues, he makes clear that the child she will bear will not be any ordinary child. Gabriel's words echo the famous promise God made to King David in 2 Samuel 7 to establish an everlasting dynasty through David's descendants.

a. Read **2 Samuel 7:9-16**; then review **Luke 1:31-33**. Record the similar phrases in the box below.

God's Promise to David 2 Samuel 7:9-16		Gabriel's Announcement to Mary Luke 1:32-33	
2 Samuel 7:9	God controls Lives of people Protects the faith full	**Luke 1:32**	Zecharia - Angel Elizabeth pregnant
2 Samuel 7:14	God will destroy his enemies - give power to his king	**Luke 1:32**	Peace - Lord with you -
2 Samuel 7:13	sons did not respect offering	**Luke 1:32**	Bear son of the most High
2 Samuel 7:16		**Luke 1:33**	King of the decendants of Jacob

b. How might these Old Testament Scripture passages shed light on what the angel Gabriel is telling Mary about the child she will bear?

5. Read **Luke 1:34-35.** Awed by the angel's announcement, Mary wonders how it can be true—particularly because she is a virgin.[4]

   a. How does the angel respond to Mary's question?

   Holy Spirit + God's power will rest on Mary

   b. *Catechism* **Connection:** Read **CCC 485 and 723.** What do these paragraphs add to your understanding?

6. Read **verses 36-37.** Here, the angel informs Mary of Elizabeth's miraculous pregnancy with John the Baptist. What details are given to Mary about Elizabeth's pregnancy, and how might they strengthen Mary's faith and provide reassurance?

   The impossible fact that Elizabeth is pregnant shows God's power & humbles Mary

Mary, Servant of the Lord (Luke 1:38)

7. Read **verse 38.** In response to God's call in her life, Mary refers to herself as a "handmaid of the Lord." The word for handmaid *(doule)* refers to a servant or slave.

   a. Think about what it means to be a servant or slave. What does Mary's description of herself as a servant of the Lord and her response, "Let it be [done] to me according to your word," tell us about how she views her relationship with God?

   Mary is God's servant + puts her trust in God

   b. Read **Matthew 6:10.** How does Mary's response in **Luke 1:38** relate to the way Jesus teaches us to pray?

   Kingdom Come - will be done

   c. Read **Luke 22:42.** How does Mary's response relate to Jesus' own example?

   Gods will not Jesus will

---

[4] Text note: The Revised Standard Version–Catholic Edition (RSV-CE) translates verse 34 as, "since I have no husband." However, the original Greek more literally reads, "since I do not know man." We have already seen that Mary's betrothal to Joseph means that they are legally married, but not yet living together. To "know a man" is a biblical euphemism for sexual relations. Hence, the New American Bible (NAB) translates this verse, "How can this be, since I have no relations with a man?"

D. Application

After considering the question for reflection, commit to respond to God in a practical way and then close with prayer.

Reflect

Mary's example challenges us to examine how we live our lives. Do we truly seek God's plan for our lives, like Mary, or do we pursue our own plans, interests, desires, and comforts? Mary does not live for herself, but for God, and her example invites us to do the same.

Commit

What are some practical ways you can live your relationship with God more like Mary does—as a servant of the Lord? Each day, we should ask God what he wants for our lives—in our marriages, in our families, in our friendships, in our work, in our moral lives, and most important of all, in our relationship with him. Write down one thing you can do this week, and determine to do it with God's help.

Pray

Making a prayer of surrender, of submitting our lives to God's plan like Mary does, is something we should do at various points in our lives. Here is one prayer along these lines, written by St. Ignatius of Loyola.

Take, Lord, and receive all my liberty, my memory, my understanding, and my entire will, all I have and call my own.

You have given all to me. To you, Lord, I return it.

Everything is yours; do with it what you will. Give me only your love and your grace, that is enough for me.

Session Two *Talk Notes*

The Annunciation

I. The Greeting of Archangel Gabriel (Luke 1:28)

    A. "Hail"

        1. Alternate translation: "rejoice"

        2. Old Testament background

            a. Call of prophets for Israel to rejoice over the coming King (Messiah)

            b. Zechariah 9:9; Zephaniah 3

    B. "Full of grace"

        1. Denotes Mary has received the great gift of God's grace

        2. Grace that brings about redemption, salvation

        3. Similar word used in Ephesians 1:6-8

            a. Grace transforms the soul, bringing about redemption and forgiveness of sins

            b. The angel is saying Mary has this kind of grace within

        4. "Full of grace" tense: in the past, continues to the present

        5. Given to Mary as a title

    C. Dogma of Immaculate Conception

        1. Mary conceived full of grace in her mother's womb

        2. Mary given this gift in anticipation of Christ's salvific work

        3. God does this not for Mary's sake but as fitting preparation for her role as Mother of the Son of God

II. Mary's Response (Luke 1:29)

    A. "Greatly troubled" by Gabriel's words, "The Lord is with you"

        1. Contrast with Zechariah's fear at seeing the angel (1:12)

2. Something big will be asked of her

    a. Old Testament usage: setting someone apart for a crucial role

    b. Example: Joshua, Gideon, Moses

B. Mary rises above her emotions

1. Mary "considers" Gabriel's words

    a. She remains in "dialogue" with God

    b. Benedict XVI: "Mary enters into an interior dialogue with the Word. ... She speaks to it and lets it speak to her in order to fathom its meaning"[5]

2. Mary is troubled but not enslaved by fear

III. Gabriel's Message (Luke 1:30-35)

A. "You have found favor with God"

1. Old Testament usage: to people given great responsibility

B. "You will bear a son"

1. Echoes images from 2 Samuel 7 (promise to David of eternal kingdom)

2. Mary will conceive by the power of the Holy Spirit

IV. Mary's Response (Luke 1:38)

A. "I am the handmaid of the Lord" (Luke 1:38)

1. Handmaid = servant

2. Motivated by love

3. Mary sees life as a gift to give back to God

B. *Fiat:* "May it be done to me according to your word" (NAB)

1. The joyful embracing of God's desire with the heart of a lover

2. Mary as a model for us

---

[5] *Credo for Today: What Christians Believe* (Ignatius, 2009), 62.

Session Three

The Visitation

Luke 1:39-56

Annunciation | Visitation | Nativity | Presentation & Finding | Wedding | At the Cross | Crowning

*"Blessed are you among women, and
blessed is the fruit of your womb!"*

A. Review the Context

In the previous session, we saw that God, through the angel Gabriel, gradually reveals to Mary her mission. First, the angel's unique greeting to Mary signals to her that she is being called to an extraordinary mission. She is called to "rejoice" like Daughter Zion over the coming of Israel's King. She is "full of grace," endowed with a unique gift of God's grace in her life. And she is told that "the Lord is with you"—an expression used in the Bible to greet those God has called to play a crucial role in his plan of salvation. The angel goes on to give the specifics of Mary's mission: She is called to be the mother of the Messiah (verses 30-33); she will conceive this child not through natural means, but by the power of the Holy Spirit (verses 34-35); and this child will be the holy "Son of God" (verse 35). In verse 37, Mary is given the assurance that "with God nothing will be impossible" as she is informed of her elderly kinswoman Elizabeth's miraculous pregnancy. And Mary responds with tremendous faith, describing herself as a servant (slave) of the Lord who ardently seeks to do God's will (verse 38).

Now, we will accompany Mary on her visit to Elizabeth in a scene known as the "Visitation" (Luke 1:39-56).

Visitation, by Domenico Ghirlandaio

In this painting by Domenico Ghirlandaio (c. 1491), the aged Elizabeth—six months pregnant with John the Baptist—falls to her knees to greet her cousin, Mary. Nazareth can be seen in the distance through the arch behind them. Mary's trip would not have been a leisurely weekend vacation. She would have traveled some eighty miles south to the hill country of Judea, and the Bible tells us she stays for three months (Luke 1:56). We will consider why Mary goes "with haste" to visit Elizabeth and the significance of Elizabeth's greeting to Mary: "Blessed ... among women" and "mother of my Lord"—honorable titles that had not been given to anyone in Israel for centuries. Next, we will look at Mary's response of praise in a prayer known as the Magnificat (verses 46-55). And finally, we will consider how Luke narrates Mary's visit to Elizabeth in ways that recall a famous journey made by the Ark of the Covenant—the sacred vessel over which God's holy presence dwelt in the Old Testament. Why does the Bible associate Mary with the Ark of the Covenant and what does this tell us about her? These are some of the topics we will explore in this session.

B. Read the Story

Read the account of Mary's visit to Elizabeth in **Luke 1:39-56.**

C. Take a Deeper Look

Answering the following questions will help you understand the praise Elizabeth bestows upon Mary in **Luke 1:42-45**—words that reveal Mary to be the most important woman in salvation history—as well as the praise Mary gives to God in her exemplary prayer in verses 46-55, known as the Magnificat.

"Blessed Among Women" (Luke 1:38-45)

1. Read **Luke 1:38-45.** (If you are not familiar with the story of Elizabeth, also read **Luke 1:1-25.**) Why do you think Mary goes "with haste" (verse 39)? What might this reveal about her character?

   Elizabeth - in 6th month
   Concern for Elizabeth = caring - lo

2. **a.** In verse 42, Elizabeth says to Mary, "Blessed are you among women." Only two other women in the Bible are given this kind of praise: Jael and Judith. Read the following passages and note why they are called "blessed among women."

   Judges 5:24-26 (Sisera was the general of the Canaanite army):

   Jael killed Sisera who was killing the Israelites

   Judith 13:18 (The Assyrian general mentioned here is Holofernes):

   Judith killed Holofernes & saved the Israelites

b. Think About It: Genesis 3:15, the first messianic prophecy in the Bible, stands in the background of this passage. In that text, God announces that "the woman's seed" will crush ("bruise" or "strike") the head of the serpent (which symbolizes the devil). Given this, why might Mary be associated with Jael and Judith? What do you think she has in common with these heroines of the Old Testament who also are described as "blessed among women"?

Mary's off spring "Jesus" Saved us from sin & Evil
with out Mary . ??

3. While God is often described as "Lord" or "the LORD" in the Old Testament, in verse 43, Elizabeth refers to Mary as "the mother of my Lord." Read **2 Samuel 24:21.**

   a. To whom is the expression "my Lord" addressed in this verse?

   b. In light of this background, what is Elizabeth saying about Mary when she addresses her as "the mother of my Lord"?

4. The mother of the king played an important role in the Davidic kingdom in the Old Testament: that of the queen mother. In ancient near-eastern societies like the kingdom of Judah, the king often had many wives, some of whom had been given to him in marriage in the process of cementing political alliances with neighboring kingdoms. But each king had only one mother, and the queenship was given to her. Read the following passages, and note the ways in which the Bible depicts the authority of the mother of the king.

   1 Kings 2:19-20: *— bowed - great reverence - would not refuse a request*

   2 Kings 24:12: *So Mother was with him when surrender*

   Proverbs 31:1-12:
   Advice to King Lemuel
   No wine. Speak up for people who can not speak - wife

5. "Hail Mary, full of grace, the Lord is with thee. Blessed art thou among women and blessed is the fruit of thy womb, Jesus"—The Hail Mary prayer begins with two sentences we see in our reading in Luke. The angel Gabriel greets Mary with the first, and Elizabeth calls out the second as Mary approaches her. Write the rest of the prayer below. What connection do you see between the words of the Hail Mary and the role of the queen mother? (For further insight, read **CCC 2676–2677.**)

The Magnificat (Luke 1:46-55)

Luke 1:46-55 is known as the Magnificat, taken from the first word in the Latin translation of this verse: Magnificat Anima Mea Dominum ("my soul magnifies the Lord"). The many Catholics around the world who pray Evening Prayer in the Church's Liturgy of the Hours recite this prayer of Mary daily.

6. Read **Luke 1:46-55.**

   a. In verses 46-49, who is the recipient of God's blessings, and how has this person been blessed?

   Mary - all people will call her happy

   b. In the second half of Mary's prayer (verses 50-55), the focus changes. Who receives God's blessing in verses 50-55, and how?

   lifted the lonely - hungry - mercy to Abraham & his descendants

   c. Think About It: What do you think might be the connection between the first and second halves of Mary's prayer?

   fear of God

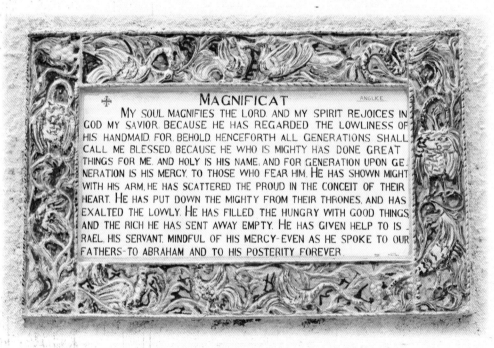

In the courtyard of the Church of the Visitation in Ein Karem, the beloved hymn of Mary known as "the Magnificat" is written on ceramic tile in fifty-seven different languages.

Mary as "Ark of the Covenant"

7. In the Visitation scene, Luke's Gospel portrays Mary as making a journey that is similar to the one made by the Ark of the Covenant in 2 Samuel 6. The Ark of the Covenant in ancient Israel is the sacred vessel that carries the stone tablets of the Ten Commandments; the staff of Aaron, the first high priest; and a jar containing the manna from the desert. Most importantly, it is associated with the holy presence of God, which hovers over the Ark.

   a. Re-read **Luke 1:39-43, 56;** then read **2 Samuel 6:2, 9-16.** Answer these questions, noting the parallels between the two scenes. The first question has been done for you.

> "The Virgin Mary is the living shrine of the Word of God, the Ark of the New and Eternal Covenant. ... In the womb of the new daughter of Zion, the Lord establishes his perfect temple in order to have full communion with mankind through his Son, Jesus Christ."[1]
>
> [1] Pontifical Council for the Pastoral Care of Migrants and Itinerant People. *The Shrine: Memory, Presence and Prophecy of the Living God* 18.

2 Samuel 6:2, 9-16 David and the Ark of the Covenant	Luke 1:39-43, 56 Mary on Her Way to See Elizabeth
Where is the Ark of the Covenant? (verse 2) *The Ark is in Baale-judah (which refers to the hill country of Judah).*	**To where is Mary traveling? (verse 39)** *Mary is going to a city in the hill country of Judea (Judah).*
What question does David ask about the Ark? (verse 9) How can he take Ark convenant with him	**What does Elizabeth ask about Mary? (verse 43)** Why the Lords moter come to her
Where does the Ark stay? (verse 10) Obed Edom Levite Pries	**Where does Mary stay? (verse 40)** Zecharia's house Levite Priest
How long does the Ark stay there? (verse 11) 3 month	**How long does Mary stay there? (verse 56)** 3 month
How does David react to the LORD's presence in the Ark? (verse 16) danced - sacrifices + shared fuod	**How does the baby in Elizabeth's womb react to the Lord's presence in Mary? (verse 41)** baby jumped - leaped

    b. What do you think these parallels tell us about Mary? See also **CCC 2676,** under the subheading, *"Full of grace, the Lord is with thee."*

D. Application

After considering the question for reflection, commit to respond to God in a practical way and then close with prayer.

Reflect

In her prayer known as the Magnificat, Mary exemplifies how all Christians should praise and give thanks to God. Re-read **Luke 1:46-49.** Prayerfully consider the ways in which God has been your Savior. In what ways has he looked upon your own lowliness? How has he done great things for you?

Commit

How might you be able to use Mary's words to praise God for what he has done in your own life? Write your answer, along with the times this week you will set aside to offer your own praise to God.

Pray

Use the words of Mary's Magnificat (Luke 1:46-55) to inspire you to praise and thank the Lord like she does.

The Magnificat

"My soul magnifies the Lord, and my spirit rejoices in God my Savior, for he has regarded the low estate of his handmaiden, For behold, henceforth all generations will call me blessed; for he who is mighty has done great things for me, and holy is his name. And his mercy is on those who fear him from generation to generation. He has shown strength with his arm, he has scattered the proud in the imagination of their hearts, he has put down the mighty from their thrones, and exalted those of low degree; he has filled the hungry with good things, and the rich he has sent empty away. He has helped his servant Israel, in remembrance of his mercy, as he spoke to our fathers, to Abraham and to his posterity for ever." – Luke 1:46-55

Glory be to the Father and to the Son and to the Holy Spirit. As it was in the beginning, is now and ever shall be, world without end. Amen

Session Three *Talk Notes*

The Visitation

I. Mary Goes "in Haste" to Visit Elizabeth (Luke 1:39-40)

   A. To help Elizabeth in her pregnancy

   B. In faith, to see the sign of what God is doing

II. Elizabeth Greets Mary with Titles of Honor (Luke 1:41-45)

   A. "Blessed are you among women" – Old Testament background:

   1. Jael and Judith: "blessed among women" for crushing the head of enemy leaders

   2. Mary's connection to them: fulfillment of Genesis 3:15

   a. Messianic prophecy: The woman will have a son who will crush ("bruise" or "strike") the head of the Serpent

   B. "Mother of my Lord" – Old Testament background:

   1. "My Lord" refers to the king

   2. Ancient near East: The king's mother reigned as queen

   3. Mary as "Queen Mother" is seen in three ways

   a. A queen's royal authority (see Jeremiah 13:18; 2 Kings 24)

   b. Counselor to the king (see Proverbs 31)

   c. Advocate for the people (see 1 Kings 1–2, change in Bathsheba's role as Solomon takes the throne)

   4. Mary as Queen Mother

   a. Queen of heaven and earth

   b. Intercessory role

   C. "Blessed is she who believed" – New Testament perspective

   1. Luke: A faithful disciple is one who hears the Word of God and keeps it

2. Mary revealed as first who hears and keeps God's Word

3. Elizabeth honors Mary for her belief: the model faithful disciple

III. Mary's Journey Shows Her to Be the "New Ark of the Covenant"

A. Ark held stone tablets, Aaron's staff, manna; God's presence

B. Mary's journey parallels journey made by Ark (2 Samuel 6)

1. From the hill country of Judea

2. David asks, "How can the ark of the Lord come unto me?"

3. Ark resides three months at Obed-Edom's house and blesses it

4. David dances, leaps before the Ark

5. Key connection: Luke 1:42, Elizabeth "exclaimed"

a. Gk., *anaphoneo* used just one time in New Testament; six times in Greek Old Testament (Septuagint), each to describe Levites praising God before the Ark

C. Mary is the new ark, carrying the new manna, the fulfillment of the Law, the true High Priest, the presence of God

D. Application to today

IV. The Magnificat (Luke 1:46-55)

A. A "narrative pause" in Luke's action

B. Two parts

1. First part focuses on the Lord's blessings to Mary

2. Second part describes God's coming blessings to Israel

C. Connection: the theme of reversal – the lowly will be exalted

1. Part two foreshadows Jesus' public ministry

V. Imitate Mary's Humility ["Magnify" = "to Make Great" (Greek)]

Grotto of the Church of the Nativity, Bethlehem

Session Four
The Nativity

Luke 2:1-20

Annunciation · Visitation · Natitivity · Presentation & Finding · Wedding · At the Cross · Crowning

"And [Mary] gave birth to her first-born son ..."

A. Review the Context

In the previous session, we considered how Elizabeth praises Mary as the most significant woman in salvation history. Indeed, Mary is "blessed among all women" and "the mother of my Lord," pointing to Mary's unique role as the mother of the King—the Queen Mother. We also saw that Mary, in a prayer known as the Magnificat, praises God in thanksgiving for all he is accomplishing in her life and in Israel. The first half of Mary's prayer focuses on God looking on her lowliness and exalting her to be the Mother of the Messiah, while the second half praises God for looking mercifully on all the poor and suffering people in Israel and exalting them. Indeed, what God does in Mary anticipates what God wants to do for all his people. Finally, we considered how the Visitation scene presents Mary's journey to Elizabeth in several ways that recall the famous journey made by the Ark of the Covenant in the Old Testament. Luke's Gospel, thus, reveals Mary to be a new Ark of the Covenant.

Now we go on another journey with Mary, this time from Nazareth to Bethlehem, where she will deliver the holy child Jesus. This trip to Bethlehem is not something she has planned. She is uprooted from her home in Nazareth so that Joseph can take part in the Roman census that requires him to be counted in his ancestral town. We will consider the full picture of Mary's experience at the birth of her son.

We will see how this difficult move near the end of her pregnancy affects Mary and discuss the sorrow any mother would feel about her newborn baby being born in the manger

Mary's Firstborn:
Did Mary Have Other Children?

The dogma of Mary's perpetual virginity proclaims that Mary remained a virgin throughout her life (see CCC 499).

"Against this doctrine the objection is sometimes raised that the Bible mentions brothers and sisters of Jesus.[1] The Church has always understood these passages as not referring to other children of the Virgin Mary. In fact James and Joseph, 'brothers of Jesus,' are the sons of another Mary, a disciple of Christ, whom St. Matthew significantly calls 'the other Mary.'[2] They are close relations of Jesus, according to an Old Testament expression"[3] (CCC 500).

[1] Cf. Mark 3:31-35, 6:3; 1 Corinthians 9:5; Galatians 1:19.
[2] Matthew 13:55, 28:1, cf. Matthew 27:56.
[3] Cf. Genesis 13:8, 14:16, 29:15, etc.

Nativity, by Nichlaas de Liemaeckere

because there was no room in the inn. Mary responds to the mysterious events surrounding Christ's birth by keeping all these things and pondering them in her heart. We will look at what it means for Mary to "keep and ponder" and examine the significance of Mary bearing her child in the city of Bethlehem; of her child being described by the angels as "Savior"; and the meaning of her baby being wrapped in swaddling cloths and laid in a manger. All of these details are charged with great symbolism and meaning in the Bible.

What Are "Swaddling Cloths"?

Swaddling cloths are strips of cloth wrapped around a baby to restrict its movements and keep it quiet—not unlike the way newborns are wrapped snugly in light blankets today. The mention of swaddling cloths in Luke's account may be a reference to Wisdom 7:3-5, in which Solomon says, "My first sound was a cry, like that of all. I was nursed with care in swaddling cloths. For no king has had a different beginning of existence." If so, the image may call to mind Solomon, the first "son of David" to sit on Israel's throne and the son through whom David's royal line is established. Now in Bethlehem is born his long-awaited heir, wrapped in swaddling cloths.

B. Read the Story

Read the account of the trip to Bethlehem and Jesus' birth in **Luke 2:1-20.**

C. Take a Deeper Look

Answering the following questions will help you understand Mary's experience of the events surrounding the birth of her son in Bethlehem.

The Roman Census (Luke 2:1-7)

We see in the Annunciation account that Mary is the Mother of the Messiah, the Mother of the Son of God. And the Visitation scene reveals her to be "most blessed among women," the Queen Mother in her son's kingdom, and the new Ark of the Covenant bearing the presence of God. Now the story of the Nativity presents for the first time the trials and sufferings Mary will experience in her maternal mission as she gives birth to Jesus in conditions of poverty, humility, and rejection.

> ## Mary, Mother of God
>
> "The One whom [Mary] conceived as man by the Holy Spirit, who truly became her Son according to the flesh, was none other than the Father's eternal Son, the second person of the Holy Trinity. Hence the Church confesses that Mary is truly 'Mother of God'" *(Theotokos).*[4]
>
> [4] CCC 495; Council of Ephesus (431): DS 251.

1. Read **Luke 2:1-5.** Notice that Luke spends more time discussing the background circumstances than he spends on describing the details surrounding the birth of Jesus. In this way, Luke draws our attention to something in the historical context that he thinks is important to understanding the story of Christ's birth. What key word is used four times in these five verses?

   Cencus - Register

2. The Romans use a census to pay for their rule over the land. This particular census requires people to return to their ancestral hometowns. So Mary suddenly must travel with Joseph from Nazareth to Bethlehem, a journey of perhaps four or five days on foot, presumably in the last trimester of her pregnancy. Read **Luke 2:4-7** carefully, putting yourself in the place of Mary.

   a. What do you think Mary is going through as she journeys to Bethlehem for the census?

   Will this baby be born -

   b. What do you think it is like for Mary to find "no place for them in the inn" and to deliver her child in these conditions? What emotions might she experience, and why?

To Keep and Ponder (Luke 2:8-19)

3. Jesus is born in humility and poverty; but in the region around Bethlehem, God's glory shines out and angels fill the sky, praising God and announcing the birth of the Savior to shepherds as they watch over their flocks. Read **Luke 2:8-19** carefully, focusing on **verse 19.** What is Mary's overall response to the events surrounding her son's birth—the trials, the poverty, and the humility of the Messiah's birth and the extraordinary testimony of the shepherds?

   Amazed - thought deeply

4. **Old Testament Connection:** This idea of keeping and pondering in the heart is found several times in the Old Testament.

   a. Read **Genesis 37:5-11.** What is the difference between the response of Joseph's brothers to his puzzling dream and the response of Joseph's father, Jacob (verse 11)?

   envy & hate
   Father - scolde but worry

   b. Read **Proverbs 3:1-2.** What does the father in this proverb want his son to do?

   don't forget what he has been taught

   c. Read **Psalm 119:11.** What does the psalmist want to do with God's Word, and why?

   Keep law in heart - will follow

5. Given the ways this idea of keeping and pondering is used in the Old Testament, what do you think it means for Mary to keep and ponder in her heart all that has happened in the events surrounding Jesus' birth?

The Mysteries Surrounding Christ's Birth

6. One aspect of the mystery surrounding Christ's birth is that Mary is forced by the Roman-decreed census to travel to Bethlehem. There is deep meaning in this move. Bethlehem is a city associated with royalty. It is the city from which King David came and a city that has taken on great importance for Israel's future hopes. Read **Micah 5:2-4**[5] (NAB 5:1-3) and answer the following questions.

   a. What does Micah's prophecy say will take place in Bethlehem?

   ruler of Israel

---

[5] Micah prophesied in the southern kingdom of Judah around the time the northern kingdom fell to Assyria and many of the people were taken into exile. He warned that a similar fate would befall Judah should they fail to repent and return to the Lord, while also foreseeing a day when a remnant of the exiles would be re-gathered and restored in Israel. It is this future return that these verses evoke.

b. In light of this prophecy, how does God use the Roman census to serve a good purpose?

to fullfill prophecy

7. Another aspect of the mystery of Christ's birth is the angel's announcement of "good news ... to all the people," the birth of a Savior that causes the angelic hosts to proclaim peace on earth (Luke 2:10-14). In the first century, Caesar has been known as the "savior of the world" and as a "son of God," one who has brought "good news" of "peace" throughout the world. His birthday has been celebrated throughout the empire as the start of a new era.

Re-read **Luke 2:8-14**. In light of this background, what does the angel's announcement tell us about Mary's child, and how do these verses of Luke's Gospel subvert the imperial propaganda regarding Caesar?

Savior was born - Christ the Lord

8. Luke makes a point of highlighting the humility, poverty, and rejection surrounding Christ's birth. This is a mystery that Mary will come to understand more profoundly years later, when her son is taken down from the Cross on Good Friday. Re-read **Luke 2:7**. Then read **Luke 23:53** and answer the following questions. Pay particular attention to the verbs that are used in both verses.

a. What happens to Jesus' body when it is taken down from the Cross?

Wrapped in linens & put in private tomb

b. How is this similar to what happens to Jesus at his birth?

wrapped in swaddle

A cave in The Shepherds' Field, Bethlehem

   c. In light of this literary connection, what might Luke be trying to tell us about God's Son?

9. *Catechism* **Connection:** Mary, in her humble maternity, is the model for us all. Read **CCC 563 and 725.** What does this mean for us as we seek to accept Jesus and bear his life into the world?

St. John Paul II Reflects on the Way Mary Shares in Her Son's Redeeming Mission

"Mary experiences childbirth in a condition of extreme poverty: she cannot give the Son of God even what mothers usually offer a newborn baby; instead, she has to lay him 'in a manger,' an improvised cradle which contrasts with the dignity of the 'Son of the Most High.'

"The Gospel notes that 'there was no place for them in the inn' (Luke 2:7). This statement, recalling the text in John's Prologue: 'His own people received him not' (John 1:11), foretells as it were the many refusals Jesus will meet with during his earthly life. The phrase 'for them' joins the Son and the Mother in this rejection, and shows how Mary is already associated with her Son's destiny of suffering and shares in his redeeming mission."

– St. John Paul II, General Audience, November 20, 1996

D. Application

After considering the question for reflection, commit to respond to God in a practical way and then close with prayer.

Reflect

Put yourself in Mary's shoes. She is the mother of Israel's King, the mother of God's Son. She is Queen Mother and "blessed among women." Even so, near the end of her pregnancy she is forced to uproot from Nazareth and move far to the south to Bethlehem, where she gives birth to Jesus in a poor and humble setting that would be unwelcoming for any newborn and that is certainly unfit for a king. Mary is not treated the way she deserves, and her royal son is not welcomed as he should be. Yet, we never read about Mary complaining or demanding better treatment. Instead, she turns to the Lord and prayerfully keeps "all these things, pondering them in her heart" (Luke 2:19).

How do you respond when you are not treated the way you think you should be? When you are not appreciated? When things do not go the way you hoped?

Commit

What can you learn from Mary's example? Name one or two practical ways that Mary's example inspires you to respond virtuously to poor treatment at work, in your parish, from a family member, or from a friend. Prayerfully commit to act on what you have learned at the next opportunity.

Pray

We looked last week at Mary's Magnificat, in which she recalls her "low estate" and God's might. Make it your prayer again this week, particularly as you strive to carry out those things you determined to do above.

The Magnificat

"My soul magnifies the Lord, and my spirit rejoices in God my Savior, for he has regarded the low estate of his handmaiden, For behold, henceforth all generations will call me blessed; for he who is mighty has done great things for me, and holy is his name. And his mercy is on those who fear him from generation to generation. He has shown strength with his arm, he has scattered the proud in the imagination of their hearts, he has put down the mighty from their thrones, and exalted those of low degree; he has filled the hungry with good things, and the rich he has sent empty away. He has helped his servant Israel, in remembrance of his mercy, as he spoke to our fathers, to Abraham and to his posterity for ever." –Luke 1:46-55

Glory be to the Father and to the Son and to the Holy Spirit. As it was in the beginning, is now and ever shall be, world without end. Amen

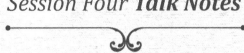

Session Four *Talk Notes*

The Nativity

I. The Context (Luke 2:1-5)

   A. Reason for move to Bethlehem: Roman census

      1. Census mentioned four times, birth mentioned one time

      2. Jesus born in context of Roman oppression

II. The Setting: The Place of Jesus' Birth in Bethlehem

   A. Bible not clear where they stayed; possibilities:

      1. "Inn" – place of lodging

      2. Home of a relative (two levels)

      3. Cave – earliest tradition

         a. Jesus laid in manger: born in humility, poverty, rejection

   B. Mary's response (Luke 2:19): to keep and ponder

III. The Significance of "Keeping" and "Pondering"

   A. Meaning of words

      1. "Ponder" = "to throw side by side"

      2. "Kept" describes one faced with a mysterious event; seeking deeper meaning so as to conform one's life

         a. Example: Genesis 37 (Jacob)

    B. Mary kept, pondered the events of the Incarnation and birth

      1. Lesson for us

      2. The reason for the move to Bethlehem

        a. Micah 5 prophecy

        b. Luke 2:7: "wrapped" and "laid" – connection to Calvary

IV. Dogma of Mary's Perpetual Virginity

    A. Contradictions in Scripture: Do these imply other children?

      1. Luke 2:7: "firstborn son"

      2. Matthew 13:55: Jesus' "brethren"

    B. Explanation of terms

      1. "Firstborn" = title for the heir; does not imply siblings

      2. "Brethren" *(adelphoi)* used elsewhere for male cousins, for an uncle and nephew, for men bound by covenant

    C. Scriptural support: John 19 – Jesus entrusts Mary to John

V. Ways to Imitate Mary (Carried Jesus in Womb, Bore Him to the World)

    A. Unite to him in prayer life

    B. Through good deeds, radiating his love

    C. After Mass, united in Holy Communion

Jerusalem, as seen from the Mount of Olives

Session Five

The Presentation &
The Finding of Jesus in the Temple

Luke 2:21-52

Annunciation · Visitation · Nativity · Presentation & Finding · Wedding · At the Cross · Crowning

" ... and a sword will pierce through your own soul also ..."

A. Review the Context

In the previous session, we considered how Mary is uprooted from Nazareth near the end of her pregnancy and has to move to Bethlehem, where she gives birth to Jesus in poor, humble conditions unfit for the newborn King of Israel. Mary's response to these trials is exemplary: She "kept all these things, pondering them in her heart" (Luke 2:19). We saw how this expression indicates that Mary prayerfully seeks to understand what the mysteries surrounding her son's birth reveal about his identity and mission. Indeed, the surprisingly humble nature of Christ's birth in Bethlehem reveals that he is the great, royal ruler of Israel prophesied by Micah (Micah 5:2), that he—and not Caesar—is the true Lord and Savior of the world, and that the way he is born into this world with humility, poverty, and rejection foreshadows how he will fulfill his mission on the Cross (Luke 2:7; 23:53).

Now we turn our attention to two scenes from Jesus' infancy and childhood that take place in the Temple in Jerusalem: the Presentation of Jesus and the account of Jesus being lost and found in the Temple. Two Jewish customs stand behind the first scene: Jews were required to present their firstborn sons at the Temple, and mothers, forty days after giving birth, were required to offer a sacrifice at the Temple for their ritual purification.

Women in Jesus' day were permitted to enter the Temple only as far as the easternmost inner area, sometimes known as the "Court of Women." Here, donations were made to the Temple treasury, including the money Mary would bring to pay for her sacrifice of two turtledoves or pigeons. According to Luke, when Mary arrives, an elderly man named Simeon greets her.

Simeon prophesies that Jesus will be a light to the nations, but he also foretells that Jesus will be "set for the rise and fall of many in Israel" and "a sign that is contradicted," and that a sword will pierce Mary's soul, also. In this session, we will consider the meaning of these stark words. They point to the violent opposition Mary's son will face and the great suffering this will bring to her soul.

Finally, we will examine the only scene of Jesus' childhood reported in any of the Gospels: the account of the boy Jesus being lost and then found three days later in the Temple. Now twelve years old, Jesus is old enough to leave the Women's Court and enter the Court of the Israelites. For the first time, he will be permitted into the area where the respected teachers of the Law convene to discuss the Scriptures. Here, we will consider how Mary and Joseph could lose their boy and the meaning of Jesus' mysterious words when they find him: "Did you not know that I must be in my Father's house?" (Luke 2:49) We will walk with Mary through this trying experience and consider how the scene foreshadows another time Mary will be separated from her son: at his death on Good Friday.

The Presentation in the Temple, by Caroline Léna Becker

B. Read the Story

Read **Luke 2:21-52,** which gives the accounts of Mary and Joseph presenting the child Jesus in the Temple as an infant and losing and finding him in the Temple when he is twelve years old.

C. Take a Deeper Look

Answering the following questions will help you understand the unique call Mary is given in this scene and her exemplary response of faith.

Obedient Parents (Luke 2:21-24)

1. Read **Luke 2:21-24.** In what ways are Mary and Joseph model and obedient Jewish parents?

2. Verse 24 reports that Mary and Joseph bring a pair of turtledoves or two young pigeons for the purification ritual. Read what the Law requires in **Leviticus 12:8.** What does this tell us about the Holy Family?

Simeon's Prophecy (Luke 2:25-35)

While at the Temple in Jerusalem, Mary encounters a man named Simeon who has the Holy Spirit upon him and who is looking for the "consolation of Israel" (Luke 2:25). He has been given the extraordinary revelation that he will not die until he sees the Lord's Christ, the Messiah (see Luke 2:26).

3. **Old Testament Connection:** Read **Luke 2:25-32,** in which Simeon takes the child Jesus in his arms and utters a prophecy about the child's greatness, using words that recall a famous prophecy from the book of Isaiah.

   a. Now read that prophecy in **Isaiah 42:1-6,** which speaks about God's Servant, the Redeemer God will send to rescue Israel. What does God say he has done with this Servant? (See verse 6b.)

   b. Read **Luke 2:32.** What does Simeon say about Jesus in this verse that recalls **Isaiah 42:6?**

   c. What would this tell Mary about her child?

4. Next, Simeon utters a prophecy specifically to Mary. Read **Luke 2:34-35.**

   a. In verse 35, Simeon speaks of a sword. Read the following Old Testament passages and note what the image of the sword is used to describe.

Leviticus 26:6:

Leviticus 26:7:

Deuteronomy 32:25:

b. In light of this background, what does the image of the sword represent in the Old Testament? And what does this tell us about Simeon's prophecy about the child Jesus in **Luke 2:33-35?**

c. Now read **John 19:31-35,** the account of Jesus' death. How does Simeon's prophecy about the sword relate to Jesus' death on the Cross?

d. Finally, what do you think Simeon's words about a sword piercing Mary's soul mean? Read also **CCC 529.**

Lost in Jerusalem (Luke 2:41-45)

Luke's next account involving Mary's life comes twelve years later, when the Holy Family is returning from their annual journey to Jerusalem for the feast of the Passover. This is one of the most important yearly feasts, and Jews from all over the ancient world would travel to Jerusalem to celebrate.

5. Read **Luke 2:41-45.** It is easy to wonder today how Mary and Joseph could leave their son behind in the big city of Jerusalem. What do these verses tell us that might shed light on how these holy and responsible parents could lose their child so easily?

The "Second Annunciation to Mary"

"Simeon's words seem like a second Annunciation to Mary, for they tell her of the actual historical situation in which the Son is to accomplish his mission, namely, in misunderstanding and sorrow. While this announcement on the one hand confirms her faith in the accomplishment of the divine promises of salvation, on the other hand it also reveals to her that she will have to live her obedience of faith in suffering, at the side of the suffering Savior, and that her motherhood will be mysterious and sorrowful."

– St. John Paul II, *Redemptoris Mater* 16

"My Father's House" (Luke 2:46-52)

6. When Mary finally finds her son three days later, she asks why Jesus has treated his parents this way. But Jesus replies, "How is it that you sought me? Did you not know that I must be in my Father's house?" (Luke 2:49)

   a. What do you think it means that Jesus must be in his Father's house? See also **CCC 534**.

   b. Read **Luke 2:50**. How well do Mary and Joseph understand these words of Jesus?

   c. Read **Luke 2:51**. What is Mary's response to this event? (See again CCC 534.)

   d. What might Mary's example teach us about how to respond when we do not understand why God allows us to experience moments of trial, uncertainty, or darkness or what God may be trying to teach us through these difficulties?

7. This experience of Mary and Jesus anticipates what will happen to them at the climax of his mission. Answer the questions in the following chart, noting how this scene from Luke 2 might prefigure the events surrounding Jesus at the culmination of his public ministry and Mary's involvement there.

Twelve-Year-Old Jesus Lost in the Temple (Luke 2:41-52)	Jesus Approaching the Culmination of His Public Ministry
Read Luke 2:41. Jesus travels from Galilee to what city?	**Read Luke 9:51**. Near the end of his public ministry, Jesus travels from Galilee to what city?
Read Luke 2:41. For what feast does Jesus travel to this city?	**Read Luke 22:1.** What feast is approaching when Jesus arrives in the city?
Read Luke 2:46. What building does Jesus visit there?	**Read Luke 19:45**. What building does Jesus visit there?

Twelve-year-old Jesus lost in the Temple (Luke 2:41-52)	Jesus approaching the culmination of his public ministry
Read Luke 2:45. What happens between Mary and Jesus while he is in this city?	**Think About It:** What happens between Mary and Jesus on Good Friday, when Jesus is crucified?
Read Luke 2:46. On what day of the week are Mary and Jesus reunited?	**Read Luke 9:22.** On what day after his death would Mary and Jesus have been reunited?

The Seven Sorrows of the Virgin, by Simon Bening

The Seven Sorrows of Mary: "And a Sword Will Pierce Through Your Own Soul Also."

We are beginning to see in this session that Mary's suffering is not limited to the intense grief she will experience during her son's passion and death, but begins in the early days of Jesus' life when Simeon proclaims that "a sword will pierce through your own soul also" (Luke 2:35). Catholic tradition remembers the "seven dolors" or "seven sorrows" of Mary[1] in the title "Our Lady of Sorrows." Sometimes they are depicted in religious art by seven swords piercing Mary's heart, recalling Simeon's prophecy. As we have seen in this session, the heart that is pierced is the same heart that holds those mysteries deep within, pondering them in the same way she received the first indication she would be the Mother of God: "Let it be to me according to your word" (Luke 1:38).

---

[1] The Seven Sorrows are the prophecy of Simeon; the flight into Egypt; the loss of the Child Jesus in the Temple; the meeting of Jesus and Mary on the Way of the Cross; the Crucifixion; the taking down of Jesus' body from the cross; and the burial of Jesus. In the Seven Sorrows devotion, it is customary to pray one Our Father and seven Hail Marys daily while meditating on each sorrow.

D. Application

After considering the question for reflection, commit to respond to God in a practical way and then close with prayer.

Reflect

Mary's experience of losing Jesus is one we might sometimes experience in our spiritual lives. We face trials that cause us anxiety. Prayer becomes dry. We wonder why these troubles have come upon us. We seek God and wonder where God is in our lives. Jesus may seem lost and far away, but in reality, he is doing the will of the Father in the temples of our souls.

Prayerfully consider a time when you felt Jesus was far away and you could not find him in your usual places (e.g., prayer, Mass, family, fellowship). Why do you think God sometimes seems distant? What does Mary's experience of losing Jesus teach you about what God is doing in these moments and how you might respond?

Commit

Resolve to reflect every day this coming week on the sufferings Mary experiences. Here are some suggestions of ways to do this: Pray the Seven Sorrows devotion every day; pray the fourth and fifth joyful mysteries of the Rosary—the Presentation and the Finding of the Child Jesus in the Temple—each day; meditate on the scriptural scenes from today's study each day (prayerfully considering what Mary goes through when she hears Simeon's words in the Temple and when she loses her son in Jerusalem).

Pray

Ask the Blessed Mother to pray for you as you ponder and seek her son's presence.

"Sorrowful and Immaculate Heart of Mary, pray for us who have recourse to thee."

Session Five **Talk Notes**

The Presentation & The Finding of Jesus in the Temple

I. **Presentation, Purification (Luke 2:22-24)**

    A. Obedience to Law

    B. The significance of the offering (two birds) – Mary and Joseph were poor

    C. Foreshadows the offering of her own son

II. **Simeon (Luke 2:25-35)**

    A. Longing for the "consolation of Israel"

        1. Jesus fulfills Isaiah (see 40:1 – "console, console my people")

    B. Told he will not die until he sees Israel's Messiah

    C. Simeon's canticle uses key words from second half of Isaiah

        1. God's salvation, a light of revelation to the Gentiles

        2. "Glory" = the visible manifestation of God's presence

            a. Exodus 40: glory cloud on Tabernacle at Mount Sinai

            b. 1 Kings 8: glory cloud fills dedicated Temple

            c. 586 BC, Ezekiel 10: glory departs Temple and Jerusalem

        3. The new ark brings God's glory, presence back to the Temple

    D. Simeon's prophecy foretells the suffering of Jesus

        1. Destined for the "rise and fall" of many

        2. A sign contradicted

        3. Revealing thoughts

E. Simeon's prophecy to Mary: "A sword will pierce your soul also"

    1. "Sword" foreshadows soldier piercing Jesus' side

        a. Mary as mother will grieve

        b. St. John Paul II: "a second Annunciation"

    2. "Soul" used only two times in Luke to describe an individual: Mary

        a. Magnificat: "My soul magnifies the Lord ..."

        b. Canticle of Simeon: "A sword will pierce your soul ..."

        c. Mary's soul will magnify the Lord by her sharing in her son's suffering

    3. Lessons for us

III. Finding Jesus in the Temple

A. How could Mary and Joseph leave him? – the cultural setting

B. Mary and Joseph search for him "anxiously"

C. Jesus' response: "... in my Father's 'house'"

    1. "House" = the Temple of the Lord; or the Father's authority, will

    2. His primary allegiance is to the Father

D. Why does Jesus cause them grief? – This scene parallels his later journey to the Cross

    1. Journey from Galilee to Jerusalem for Passover

    2. He amazes people with his teaching

    3. He does something that causes his mother grief

    4. They are reunited on the third day

    5. Why? Jesus is doing the will of the Father

E. Enter Mary's experience: a lesson for us

Franciscan Wedding Church, Cana

Session Six

The Wedding at Cana

John 2:1-11

Annunciation   Visitation   Nativity   Presentation & Finding   Wedding   At the Cross   Crowning

"Do whatever he tells you."

A. Review the Context

In the previous session on the Presentation and the finding of Jesus in the Temple, we saw that Mary is a model and obedient Jew, following the Law in her son's circumcision, in her own ritual purification, and in taking her firstborn son to be presented at the Temple (Luke 2:21-24). While at the Temple, Mary hears Simeon proclaim that her son is the fulfillment of Isaiah's prophecy of the Lord's Servant who will reunite Israel and be a light to the nations (Isaiah 42:6; Luke 2:32). But she also hears Simeon's prophecy about her son's future suffering, rejection, and death, which will result in a sword piercing her soul also (Luke 2:35). Next, we studied Mary's painful experience of losing Jesus for three days in Jerusalem—an experience that foreshadows what will happen to Jesus and Mary when Christ's public ministry reaches its climax on Calvary. At the time, this is an event that Mary does not fully understand (Luke 2:50), but which she prayerfully keeps and ponders in her heart (Luke 2:51). Perhaps she comes to appreciate its depths after she loses her son, first in Jerusalem and again when he dies on the Cross.

The Marriage at Cana, by Gerard David

Where Luke brings us up close to the Holy Family in the early years of Jesus' life, showing us his humanity, John's Gospel begins from the wide-angle viewpoint of heaven and eternity to show us Jesus, the Word, co-existent in the beginning with the Father (John 1:1-18). Where Luke helps us to see Jesus through the eyes of Mary, John now will help us see Mary through the eyes of Jesus. Not surprisingly, he skips the details of Christ's birth and jumps into the larger questions of Jesus' identity and mission. And in this wide-angle vision, Mary features briefly but prominently in the opening and closing scenes, providing a frame of sorts around John's account of the Lord's ministry (John 2:1-11, 19:25-27).

This week we look at the first of those scenes: the wedding feast at Cana, where Jesus performs his first miracle and launches his public ministry. Jesus is about thirty years old when he starts his ministry (Luke 3:23), so Mary is a mature woman by now—in her early forties, at least. This story of the wedding at Cana gives us insight not only into Mary's character, but also into the nature of her relationship with her son.

In Cana, the host of the feast is running out of wine. In first-century Judaism, to run out of wine at a wedding feast would bring great shame upon a family because it would indicate that a family was not able to provide for guests according to the social status they claim to possess. Mary is the first to notice this impending social disaster, and she goes to Jesus: "They have no wine." We will consider the significance of this act and the meaning of the words Jesus says in response: "Woman, what is this to you and to me? My hour has not yet come." We will see that these words do not imply any hostility or opposition on Jesus' part. Rather, they exalt Mary as the most important woman in salvation history, who plays a crucial role in the Messiah's mission.

Next we will consider Mary's command to the servants, "Do whatever he tells you"—a command that represents Mary's last recorded words in the Bible. We will look at how these words reflect Old Testament expressions of covenant faith and how Mary's exhortation has a profound impact on the servants.

First century stone jar, Franciscan Wedding Church, Cana

B. Read the Story

Read **John 2:1-11,** which gives the account of Mary at the wedding feast at Cana, where Jesus performs his first public miracle.

C. Take a Deeper Look

Answering the following questions will help you understand Mary's unique role in Christ's mission.

Understanding the Context (John 1:1–2:1)

John begins his account of the wedding at Cana with a phrase that is easy to overlook: "On the third day." On the third day of what? Let us back up and explore the context of John's Gospel before we go further into Chapter 2.

1. John's Gospel begins with many images from the story of Creation in Genesis 1. Read **John 1:1-5.** What are some of the ways these verses recall the story of Creation?

2. a. The Creation theme continues as John narrates a series of days that together make up a new Creation week. **John 1:19** is the first day in the narrative that reports the testimony of John the Baptist. Read that and then read about the others, which are listed in order below. For each one, record what happens and when the Gospel says the event takes place.

    John 1:29:

    John 1:35-36:

    John 1:43:

    John 2:1:

    b. Review your responses to 2.a. and count through the days until you reach the wedding at Cana. On what day in John's narration is the wedding? You may use the box on the next page to help you calculate. Write your answer in the blank space at the bottom.

	John 1:19	John 1:29	John 1:35	John 1:43	John 2:1
John's Chronological Markers	Start of John's narrative	"The next day"	"The next day"	"The next day"	"On the third day"
Day Number	Day 1	Day 2	Day 3	Day 4	Day 7
Explanation	1	1+1= ___	2+1=___	3+1=___	4+3=___
The wedding feast at Cana takes place on the _____ day.					

John lays out a carefully structured timeline of events at the start of his Gospel, culminating in the start of Jesus' public ministry at the wedding at Cana.

3. **Think About It:** Given the symbolism of the Creation story that you have seen in John's Gospel, what might John be pointing out with this symbolism involving the number of days?

No Wine, but Much Faith (John 2:1-3)

4. Read **John 2:1-3,** in which Mary brings the shortage of wine to Jesus' attention.

   a. At this point in the Gospel, Jesus has yet to perform any miracles. What might this tell us about Mary's faith in her son? See also **John 20:29.**

   b. What might Mary's example teach us?

The Woman (John 2:4-10)

5. Read **John 2:4.** How does Jesus reply to Mary's request, and what do you think of his reply?

6. Now read **John 2:5.** How does this verse suggest that Mary interprets Jesus' words?

7. Read **John 2:6-10.** Do these verses seem to indicate that Jesus is refusing Mary's request or responding positively to her petition? Explain.

8. **Old Testament Connection:** Read **Genesis 3:14-15.** These verses represent the first messianic prophecy in the Bible. In light of Genesis 3:15, what is Jesus saying about himself and about his mother when he calls her "woman"? Read also **CCC 410–411.**

"Do Whatever He Tells You" (John 2:5-11)

9. Confident that her son will answer her request, Mary says to the servants, "Do whatever he tells you" (verse 5). These words recall a theme of obedience in the Old Testament and offer rich insight into how we are called to be obedient.

    a. Read the following passages in which the people of Israel make or renew their covenant with God after having heard the Word of the LORD spoken to them. Note what the people say they will do in response to what God says.

    Exodus 19:8:

    Joshua 24:24:

    Nehemiah 5:12:

    b. How do you think this Old Testament background sheds light on Mary's instruction to the servants to "do whatever he tells you"?

    c. How might Mary's instruction inspire you to follow God's Word more closely in your life?

10. Nearby stand six stone jars, the kind used to hold water for the ceremonial washing required before a meal. Each would be large enough to hold twenty to thirty gallons of water, but they are apparently empty—possibly the water has already been used by the guests at the wedding.

    a. For each verse below, note what Jesus commands and how the servants respond.

    John 2:7:

    John 2:8:

b. How faithful do you think the servants are in responding to Jesus' commands? Explain.

c. What might the servants' exemplary response tell us about the impact of Mary's exhortation in this scene?

11. When the steward tastes the water, it has miraculously become fine wine. Read **John 2:11.**

a. What does this verse tell us about the significance of Jesus' action at the wedding feast?

b. What might this verse tell us about the role and importance of Mary in Jesus' public ministry?

Mary, Our Advocate

The wedding at Cana is our first glimpse of Mary's role as intercessor and advocate. Just as Mary notices the shortage of wine at the wedding at Cana and takes the need straight to her son, Mary our mother notices our needs before we do and takes them to Jesus. We ask for her intercession every time we pray the Hail Mary and in a special way when we pray the Rosary. In *Rosarium Virginis Mariae* 16, St. John Paul II writes:

Virgin of the Adoption,
by Jean Auguste Dominique Ingres

"In support of the prayer which Christ and the Spirit cause to rise in our hearts, Mary intervenes with her maternal intercession. 'The prayer of the Church is sustained by the prayer of Mary' (CCC 2679). If Jesus, the one Mediator, is the Way of our prayer, then Mary, his purest and most transparent reflection, shows us the Way. ...

"The Rosary is both meditation and supplication. Insistent prayer to the Mother of God is based on confidence that her maternal intercession can obtain all things from the heart of her Son. ... When in the Rosary we plead with Mary, the sanctuary of the Holy Spirit (cf. Luke 1:35), she intercedes for us before the Father who filled her with grace and before the Son born of her womb, praying with us and for us."

– St. John Paul II, *Rosarium Virginis Mariae* ("The Rosary of the Virgin Mary") 16.

D. Application

After considering the question for reflection, commit to respond to God in a practical way and then close with prayer.

Reflect

Put yourself in the scene at Cana and prayerfully imagine being one of the servants at the wedding feast. Picture Mary turning to you and saying, "Do whatever he tells you." How do those words from Mary make you feel? Are you willing to do whatever God wants in your life?

Commit

Prayerfully take time to tell Jesus you desire to do his will. Then ask him to show you something he wants for your life now, and ask him for the grace to do it.

Pray

Ask our Blessed Mother and "most gracious advocate" to intercede on your behalf, perhaps using the Hail, Holy Queen prayer we say with the Rosary.

*Hail, Holy Queen, mother of mercy, our life, our sweetness, and our hope. To thee do we cry, poor banished children of Eve; to thee do we send up our sighs, mourning and weeping in this valley of tears. Turn, then, **most gracious advocate**, thine eyes of mercy toward us, and after this, our exile, show unto us the blessed fruit of thy womb, Jesus. O clement, O loving, O sweet Virgin Mary. Pray for us, O Holy Mother of God … that we may be made worthy of the promises of Christ.*

Session Six *Talk Notes*

The Wedding at Cana

I. Mary's Crucial Role at the Launch of Jesus' Public Ministry

    A. Mary is first to notice the "wine crisis"

    B. Mary brings the problem to Jesus

II. Jesus' Response: Is He Pushing Her Away or Exalting Her?

    A. In light of immediate context, his words are not negative

        1. Mary assumes he will answer

        2. Jesus answers her request

    B. By calling her "woman," Jesus honors Mary as the "new Eve" (Genesis 3:15, the woman's descendant will defeat the devil)

        1. Objection: Jesus calls others "woman"

            a. John 4:21: Samaritan woman at the well

            b. John 20:15: Mary Magdalene on Easter Sunday

        2. Support: John sets the stage for a new Creation

            a. John 1:1-5: echoes of Genesis 1

            b. John 1:19–2:1: Cana on the seventh day

            c. On that "stage," Mary comes as "the woman" whose son will defeat the devil

    C. "What is this between you and me? My hour has not yet come"

        1. Meaning of "my hour" in John's Gospel

            a. The Cross: the hour Jesus defeats the devil

            b. Jesus' hour has not yet come

        2. "What have you to do with me?"

            a. Hebrew literature: "What is this to me and to you?"

            b. Expression can denote conflict or looking with different perspectives

        3. Is this a matter of wine, or is there a deeper meaning?

            a. Old Testament prophets: wine associated with joy of the messianic age (see Isaiah 25:6; Amos 9:13)

            b. The burden of Simeon's prophecy

            c. A pivotal moment, launching Jesus toward "his hour"

III. Mary's Response: "Do Whatever He Tells You"

    A. Obedience to the will of God

    B. Effects of Mary's intercession

        1. Servants do what Jesus asks

        2. In their actions, servants become followers of Jesus

Stone of Anointing, Church of the Holy Sepulchre, Jerusalem

Session Seven

Mary at the Cross

John 19:25-30

Annunciation · Visitation · Nativity · Presentation & Finding · Wedding · At the Cross · Crowning

"'Woman, behold, your son!' Then he said to the disciple, 'Behold, your mother!'"

Lamentation of Christ, by Maerten van Heemskerck

A. Review the Context

In the previous session, we saw how Mary notices the wine shortage at Cana and turns to the one person who can solve the crisis at hand: Jesus. We studied how Jesus' calling Mary "woman" is not disrespectful, but just the opposite. This form of address reveals Mary to be in the honorable role of the "woman" prophesied in Genesis 3:15—the woman whose son would defeat the devil (symbolized by the serpent). Indeed, Mary is revealed to be the "new Eve" as Jesus begins his public ministry. We also saw how Mary's exhortation, "Do whatever he tells you" (John 2:5), recalls the faithful response of Israel to God's Word in the Old Testament. It also motivates the servants to give prompt, perfect obedience to Jesus and inspires us to do the same in our relationship with the Lord.

John's Gospel continues to follow Jesus to the Cross, where we encounter Mary once again. In this session, we will consider what the Bible tells us about her presence there on Good Friday. We will look at the significance of Mary being described in John 19 as "standing at the cross of Jesus" on Calvary in light of what Jesus has taught about disciples following him and in light of the fact that most of the other disciples have abandoned Jesus. We

also will examine the ways John presents Mary as embodying the discipleship allegory he offers at the Last Supper in John 16:21 about a woman in labor going through great pains that are transformed into joy when she holds her child. We will see how this allegory is fulfilled most especially in Mary's experience of sorrow on Good Friday, sorrow that will be turned to joy when her son rises.

We also will reflect on the meaning of Jesus entrusting Mary into the care of the "Beloved Disciple" and see how this act sheds light on Mary's role as the spiritual mother of all Jesus' faithful disciples, whom the Beloved Disciple represents. And finally, we will examine why Jesus calling his mother "woman" in the context of the "hour" of his passion points (as it does at the wedding in Cana) to Mary's role as the new Eve—the woman whose son will defeat the devil as prophesied in Genesis 3:15.

The top of Golgotha, Church of the Holy Sepulchre

B. Read the Story

Read **John 19:25-30,** which gives the account of Mary's presence standing at the foot of the Cross at Jesus' death. For further connection with this scene of the Crucifixion, begin reading from the start of Chapter 19.

C. Take a Deeper Look

Answering the following questions will help you understand the suffering Mary experiences at Calvary and her unique spiritual mission as mother of all Christians entrusted to her by Jesus.

Standing at the Cross of Jesus (John 19:25)

1. Mary only appears twice in John's Gospel. She is first mentioned in conjunction with Jesus' miracle at the wedding at Cana: "the first of his signs," in which he reveals his glory publicly for the first time and when his disciples come to believe in him. This is the start of Jesus' public ministry. The next occasion is in **John 19:25-30,** where she appears at Jesus' death on the Cross. **Think About It:** What is significant about the fact that John records her presence at just these two events?

2. **a.** Read the following verses and answer the questions to better understand Mary's role as she stands at the foot of the cross of Jesus.

   Matthew 16:21: What does Jesus say will happen to him in Jerusalem?

   Matthew 16:24: What does Jesus say his disciples must do?

   John 16:32: While at the Last Supper, what does Jesus predict the apostles will do in the hour of his passion?

   Matthew 26:56: What do the disciples do when Jesus is arrested in the Garden of Gethsemane?

   John 19:25: What are Mary and the other women doing in this verse?

   b. What might this tell us about Mary?

c. Think back over the things you have learned about Mary so far. What might be going through Mary's mind as she stands there watching Jesus die? And what might give her the strength and grace needed to be the exemplary disciple who follows him to the Cross?

3. In **John 16:20-22,** Jesus uses the analogy of a woman giving birth to help the disciples understand that although they will experience sorrow at his suffering and death, the sorrow will turn to joy when they are reunited with him in his resurrection. Read **John 19:25-27** together with **John 16:20-22,** looking for similar words and themes. How does John describe Mary at the Cross in ways that recall the allegory of the woman in labor—revealing her as a model, faithful disciple participating in Christ's passion?

Mary and the Beloved Disciple

4. Read **John 19:25-27.** What might Jesus' entrusting of his mother to his Beloved Disciple's care tell us about the relationship Jesus has with Mary?

5. Let us now consider how this action might also point to a profound spiritual reality.

a. John's Gospel often uses individual characters to represent larger groups. For example, the Samaritan woman at the well is also seen as a representative of all Samaritans who will come to believe in Jesus. And Nicodemus, the Pharisee in John 3, represents all the Pharisees who will fail to understand Jesus and instead will oppose him. Similarly, the "Beloved Disciple" is traditionally recognized as the apostle John, but in the fourth Gospel, he also represents a larger group of people. Read the following verses in which the Beloved Disciple appears, and record what John's Gospel says about him.

John 13:25:

John 19:26:

John 20:8:

John 21:7:

b. What does this tell us about those the Beloved Disciple might represent?

c. Now read **John 19:26-27** again. Mary has been looking on as her only son dies before her eyes. What does he say to her and to the Beloved Disciple?

d. Considering what you learned in 5.a. and 5.b., how do these words expand the relationship between Jesus and Mary into something far greater? See also **CCC 501 and 2674.**

The Woman and the Hour

6. Mary's important role in God's plan of salvation also can be seen in light of the theme of "the hour" in John's Gospel. The hour of Jesus, first mentioned at the wedding at Cana when Jesus says his "hour has not yet come," reaches its climax in his passion.

a. Read the following verses and note what "the hour" describes.

John 5:25-28:

John 7:30:

John 12:23-24:

Chapel of Adam, Church of the Holy Sepulchre

John 12:27, 31-33:

b. Now review **Genesis 3:15.** What is the relationship between this prophecy and Jesus' hour as described in **John 12:31?**

c. In light of this theme of the hour, what do you think is the meaning of Jesus calling his mother "woman" in the "hour" of his passion? See also **CCC 2618.**

7. **Old Testament Connection:** The book of 2 Maccabees recalls the forced Hellenization of Jews in Palestine under the Greek ruler Antiochus Epiphanes. The resulting persecution led to courageous resistance by many of the faithful. Read **2 Maccabees 7:1-39.** In what ways might the mother in this story prefigure Mary at the Cross?

D. Application

After considering the question for reflection, commit to respond to God in a practical way and then close with prayer.

Reflect

Put yourself into the scene, and prayerfully imagine what Mary is going through on Calvary, watching her son die on the Cross. We have seen that throughout her life, Mary is open to God's Word (Luke 1:29), consents to his will (Luke 1:38), and keeps and ponders the mysteries of her son's life as they unfold before her (Luke 2:19; 2:51). Now she is invited to take one more step of trust and surrender and experience the greatest sacrifice any mother could face—the killing of her own son. Here, we see Mary give up everything, even her own son, trusting that this supreme sacrifice is all a part of God's plan. Perhaps you have experienced a great suffering or loss—if so, how might you be able to relate to Mary's sorrows?

Commit

Prayerfully consider if God is asking you to surrender an area of your life to him—to give up something, to make a change, to die more to yourself and live more sacrificially for him and the people he has placed in your life. What is he asking? What one thing can you commit to do this week to follow Mary, our model of total surrender?

Pray

Are you hurting? Mary wants to be with you in your suffering. Ask her to pray for you that God might comfort and strengthen you as he did for her on Good Friday. Do you find it difficult to surrender? Ask Mary to pray for you so that you might be more like her in not holding anything back from the Lord and living your whole life for him.

Prayer to the Mother of Sorrows

Most holy Virgin and Mother, whose soul was pierced by a sword of sorrow in the passion of thy divine Son, and who in his glorious resurrection was filled with never-ending joy at his triumph; obtain for us who call upon thee, so to be partakers in the adversities of Holy Church and the sorrows of the Sovereign Pontiff, as to be found worthy to rejoice with them in the consolation for which we pray, in the charity and peace of the same Christ our Lord. Amen.

Or: *Consider praying a decade of the Rosary, focusing on the Sorrowful Mysteries.*

The Sorrowful Mysteries

"The meaning, origin and fulfillment of man is to be found in Christ, the God who humbles himself out of love 'even unto death, death on a cross' (Philippians 2:8). The sorrowful mysteries help the believer to relive the death of Jesus, to stand at the foot of the Cross beside Mary, to enter with her into the depths of God's love for man and to experience all its life-giving power." – Blessed John Paul II, Rosarium Virginis Mariae *22*

The Sorrowful Mysteries

The Agony in the Garden

The Scourging at the Pillar

The Crowning with Thorns

The Carrying of the Cross

The Crucifixion

Mary most sorrowful, Mother of Christians, pray for us.

Session Seven *Talk Notes*

Mary at the Cross

I.   Jesus' Final Act: Entrusting Mary to the Beloved Disciple

    A. "Woman, behold, your son! ... Behold, your mother!" (John 19:26-27)

    B. For meaning, read within symbolism and Old Testament allusions of John 19

        1. Verse 24, soldiers cast lots: see Psalm 22

        2. Verse 33, soldiers do not break legs: see Exodus 12:46

        3. Verse 34, side pierced with a spear: see Zechariah 12:10

    C. Key to deeper meaning: John's portrayal of the "Beloved Disciple"

        1. John uses individual people to represent larger groups

            a. John 3: Nicodemus represents Jewish leaders

            b. John 4: Samaritan woman represents Samaritans

        2. The "Beloved Disciple" (John) represents all faithful disciples

            a. Close to Jesus at the Last Supper (John 13)

            b. The only one faithful to the end

            c. First to believe in the Resurrection (20:8)

            d. First to proclaim the risen Christ (John 21)

        3. Significance: Jesus entrusts Mary as spiritual mother to John and to the faithful Christians he represents

II. "From that Hour [John] Took Her to His Own Home" (19:27) – Spiritual Significance

    A. Theme of "the hour" in John

        1. Wedding at Cana

        2. John 7:30, 8:20: Jesus eludes arrest (his hour has not come)

        3. John 12:23, 31: the hour for him "to be glorified," when the prince of this world will be cast down

        4. "Woman, behold, your son!" (19:26): the new Eve, with her son when Genesis 3:15 is fulfilled

    B. John "took her into his own home" – deeper significance

        1. "Took" – in Greek, if referring to a person: welcomed, received

            a. John 1:17

            b. John 13:20

        2. Literally "into his own"

            a. As into his interior life, as spiritual mother

III. Mary at the Cross

    A. Discipleship associated with taking up one's cross

    B. Others ran away, Mary one of few who stayed

    C. Birth parable (John 16:20-22) puts suffering in perspective

        1. Suffering leads to rejoicing

        2. Mary embodies the parable more than anyone

    D. Recalling the prophecies: How can he be the King?

        1. St. John Paul II: the greatness of Mary's faith and assent "in the face of God's unsearchable judgments"

        2. Throughout her life, Mary called to surrender and trust

IV. Catholic Devotion to Mary

    A. Does attention to Mary distract from our relationship with Jesus?

        1. Worship (praise) versus honor (recognizing excellence, showing respect)

        2. By honoring people, we recognize God's accomplishments in their lives

        3. We praise God by praising his works

    B. Why do Catholics pray to Mary?

        1. Catholics do not pray to her as though she is divine, but ask for her intercession

        2. St. Paul exhorts us to intercede

        3. Objection: 1 Timothy 2:5 – "one mediator"

            a. "One" is not "only," but "primary"

            b. All other intercession built on the intercession of Christ

        4. Mary is in heaven, next to the throne

        5. Intercession builds the family of God

Session Eight

Mary Crowned with Glory

Revelation 12

"... and on her head a crown of twelve stars ..."

A. Review the Context

In the previous session, we explored John's account of Mary at the Cross in John 19:25-27. We saw how Mary is presented as a model, faithful disciple, standing at the cross of Jesus while most of the other disciples have abandoned him. She also embodies the woman in labor in Jesus' allegory about the sufferings and joys the disciples would experience at his death and resurrection. We saw Jesus reveal Mary to be the mother of the Beloved Disciple who represents all faithful disciples—pointing to how Mary is the spiritual mother of all Christians. Finally, we considered how Mary is the new Eve in the hour of Jesus' passion, which is the hour in which the seed of the woman defeats the devil.

Now we will explore Revelation 12, a passage packed with symbolism. This chapter relays St. John's apocalyptic vision of a great battle occurring in heaven. Four key characters emerge in this drama: a woman, her child, a dragon, and Michael the archangel. First, John sees a mysterious woman "clothed with the sun" and crowned with twelve stars. This woman then gives birth to a royal son who "rules all nations with a rod of iron." A dragon with seven heads and ten horns immediately attacks the woman's child, but her son is caught up to God and to a throne, while Michael and his angels defeat the dragon.

Like many "larger-than-life" figures in Scripture, and particularly those in apocalyptic literature, the woman in Revelation 12 is both a person and a symbol. Christians have long seen her as representing Israel or the Church, and in the Catholic tradition, the woman has often been understood to be Mary. Thus, the symbolism of Revelation 12 has been incorporated into many paintings of Mary that show her clothed with the sun, with the moon under her feet and a crown of twelve stars on her head. It also is evident in the miraculous image of Our Lady of Guadalupe found on the *tilma* of Blessed Juan Diego.

What indications in the text would support this interpretation of Mary being the woman of Revelation 12? And if the woman can, indeed, be seen as Mary, what does Revelation 12 tell us about the mother of Jesus? These are some of the questions we will explore in this session. We will see how the royal woman of Revelation 12 sheds light on Mary as the new Eve, on Mary as the spiritual mother of all Christians, and, most of all, on Mary as an important biblical sign reminding us of the great vocation to which we all are called and of the "crown of righteousness" that awaits all faithful followers of Christ who persevere in faith as Mary does in her life.

Our Lady of Guadalupe, Dormition Abbey, Jerusalem

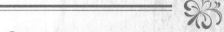

Mary, More Mother than Queen

"Mary, then, is queen, but queen in the way of a mother, serving all her children, guiding them in their most personal and intimate life, not so much by law and precept as by kindly prompting and persuasion, with an affectionate smile on her countenance as she goes about bestowing a mother's tender care on all her children, on the lowliest no less than on the more fortunate. In fact, the more humble and lowly her children, the more mother she is to them. And the more we put ourselves in Mary's guiding care, the more quickly she leads us up to God."[1]

– St. Thérèse of Lisieux

[1] St. Thérèse of Lisieux. *Novissima Verba, The Last Confidences of St. Thérèse of the Child Jesus* (Berkeley Heights, NJ: P.J. Kenedy & Sons), 1952.

B. Read the Story

Read **Revelation 12:1-17,** in which John is given a vision of "a great portent" in heaven.

C. Take a Deeper Look

Answering the following questions will help you understand why the woman in Revelation 12 should be understood at least in part as being associated with Mary and what this passage reveals about her unique role in salvation history.

The Woman and Her Child (Revelation 12:1-5)

1. Read **verses 1-4** again and describe the "portents" or "signs"[2] John sees in heaven.

2. Who is this woman? One key to understanding this is to consider the identity of the child to whom she gives birth.

    a. What does verse 5 tell us about the woman's child?

    b. Read **Psalm 2:9,** a prophetic text about the LORD's anointed King, the Messiah. What does this verse tell us about the future Messiah?

    c. In light of this background, who do you think the child is?

3. If this is true about the child, then who might the woman who gives birth to him be?

The Woman and the Dragon (Revelation 12:5-12)

4. Let us now consider how this woman is depicted here as the new Eve.

    a. Review **Genesis 3:15.** What does God say will happen between the woman described there and the serpent (a symbol for the devil)?

    b. Now read **Revelation 12:5-9.** What happens to the dragon when the woman's male child is born?

    c. According to **Revelation 12:9,** who is the dragon?

---

2   A sign in the Bible is "an act, event, or object that points beyond itself to something else, often a greater or unseen reality. Signs can serve to impart a message or key image, to give a reminder or memorial, to give an omen or portent, or to display the loving and powerful work of God." (*Catholic Bible Dictionary,* Scott Hahn, General Editor.)

d. If the dragon in Revelation 12 is the serpent of **Genesis 3:15** at the moment of his defeat, who would the "woman" be in light of this Genesis 3:15 background?

The Woman and Her Other Offspring (Revelation 12:13-17)

5. Read **Revelation 12:17.**

    a. According to this verse, the woman has other offspring. How are these other offspring described?

    b. In the vision in this verse, who are the "other offspring" on earth?

    c. Considering that the woman represents Mary, what does that suggest about Mary's relationship with us? Read also **CCC 501.**

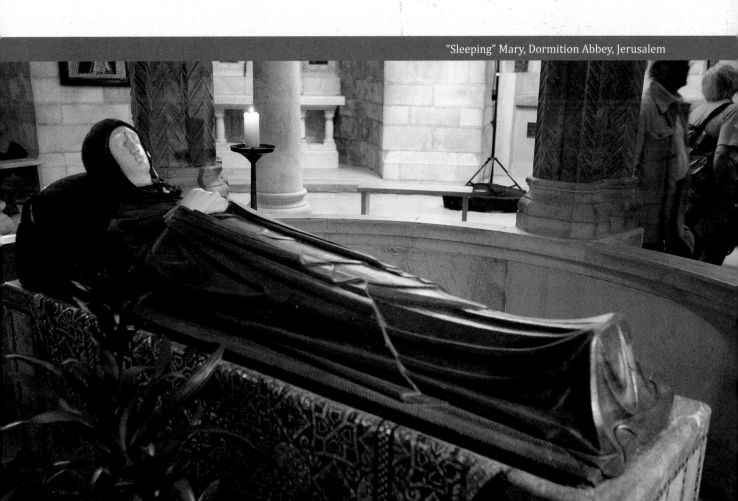

"Sleeping" Mary, Dormition Abbey, Jerusalem

The Crown of Twelve Stars

6. According to Revelation 12:1, the woman is depicted as having a crown of twelve stars on her head. Read **2 Timothy 4:7-8,** in which another heavenly crown is described.

   a. Because of what qualities does Paul say he and others will receive "the crown of righteousness" in heaven?

   b. What would this tell us about Mary, who wears a crown in Revelation 12:1?

7. Read the following passages, noting how Mary is depicted in the Bible as a persevering, faithful disciple throughout her life—and thus someone worthy of "the crown of righteousness."

   Luke 1:38:

   Luke 1:39:

   Luke 1:45:

The Sea of Galilee

Luke 2:19:

Luke 2:51:

John 19:25-27:

Acts 1:14:

8. What aspects of Mary's example of faith from the verses above inspire you the most in your own faith to pursue the crown of righteousness that awaits all Christians?

"For the Mother of Christ is glorified as 'Queen of the Universe.'[3] She who at the Annunciation called herself the 'handmaid of the Lord' remained throughout her earthly life faithful to what this name expresses. In this she confirmed that she was a true 'disciple' of Christ, who strongly emphasized that his mission was one of service: the Son of Man came not to be served but to serve, and to give his life as a ransom for many' (Matthew 20:28). In this way Mary became the first of those who, 'serving Christ also in others, with humility and patience lead their brothers and sisters to that King whom to serve is to reign,'[4] and she fully obtained that 'state of royal freedom' proper to Christ's disciples: to serve means to reign!"

– *Redemptoris Mater* 41

[3] Second Vatican Council, *Lumen Gentium* ("Dogmatic Constitution on the Church") 59.
[4] Ibid 36.

D. Application

After considering the question for reflection, commit to respond to God in a practical way and then close with prayer.

Reflect

At the end of this study, let us remember Jesus' last words about Mary in the Bible: "Behold, your mother" (John 19:27). We saw how he speaks those words to the Beloved Disciple just before he dies, entrusting him into a special relationship with Mary as his mother. But we also saw how the Beloved Disciple represents all faithful disciples of the Lord and how all Christians are given Mary as their spiritual mother.

Prayerfully ponder this scene and imagine that you are the Beloved Disciple standing next to Mary under the cross of Christ. Picture Jesus speaking these words now specifically to you, "Behold, your mother." Jesus is giving you Mary, his own mother, as your spiritual mother. What would you say to Jesus in response to this great gift? What would you say to Mary?

Commit

What can you do now to welcome Mary more into your daily life and develop a more intimate relationship with her, knowing that she, in her maternal love for you, constantly looks out for your needs and ardently prays for them to her son, Jesus? Decide to do something this week, and write it here along with when you plan to do it.

Pray

Spend a few moments thanking Mary for her maternal care. Pray the Hail Mary slowly and carefully, paying attention to the words in light of all you have learned in this study.

Hail Mary, full of grace, the Lord is with thee; blessed art thou among women, and blessed is the fruit of thy womb, Jesus. Holy Mary, Mother of God, pray for us sinners, now and at the hour of our death. Amen.

Session Eight *Talk Notes*

Mary Crowned with Glory

I. **"The Woman" of Revelation 12 Reveals Mary's Heavenly Destiny**

   A. John's vision of a great battle: three figures

      1. Woman (verses 1-2)

      2. Dragon (verses 3-4)

      3. Male child (verses 4-5)

   B. Identifying the figures

      1. The male child = Jesus

         a. Ruling with a rod of iron: messianic – Psalm 2:9

         b. Taken up to God and his throne

      2. The Dragon = Satan (12:9)

      3. Who is the woman? Various views

         a. Personification of the New Testament Church (see verses 13-17)

         b. Recalls Old Testament people of Israel and "Daughter Zion" prophecies

         c. What "woman" spans both Old Testament and New Testament?

            i. Mary represents Israel

            ii. Mary represents the Church

      4. Parallels between John 19 (Mary at Cross) and Revelation 12

         a. Both called "woman"

         b. Image of birth "pangs"

         c. Genesis 3:15 imagery fulfilled

         d. Two kinds of maternity

II. What this Tells Us About Mary

    A. Spiritual mother of all Christians: Revelation 12:17

    B. Mary's queenship

        1. Not an honorific position but a sign (a share in Christ's reign)

        2. Paul: If we persevere, we will be crowned in glory (2 Timothy 4:7-8)

        3. What God gives to Mary he intends for us

III. The Dogma of the Assumption

    A. Mary taken up body and soul into heaven at end of earthly life

    B. Scriptural precedent

        1. Enoch (Hebrews 11:5)

        2. Elijah (2 Kings)

        3. New Testament: All faithful followers of Christ will share in his victory

    C. The Magnificat: What God did in Mary foreshadows what he will do in the rest of his people

    D. Mary's last moment: entrusting herself to God

IV. Conclusion: Reflection on the Hail Mary

    A. A Scriptural prayer

    B. Addressed to Mary, but centered on Jesus

        1. First half: praising God for the Incarnation

            a. Gabriel

            b. Elizabeth

        2. Second half: asking her intercession

        3. At the heart: the holy name of Jesus

MARY

A Biblical Walk with the Blessed Mother

Responses to the Study Questions

How to Use These Responses

After completing the home preparation, discussing the questions, and viewing the video presentation, the final step is to review the responses to the questions. These responses summarize the main points from the session and help you continue your Bible study in the next session.

Although it can be tempting to read these responses ahead of time, please wait until after you have completed the questions for each session and engaged in the small-group discussion. It is not necessary to have the "right" answers before going to the small-group discussion. In fact, one purpose of the discussion is for participants to learn by sharing their insights and questions with each other and, through that discussion, coming to a better understanding of the Scripture passages. This makes for a better Bible study experience for everyone.

For best results, follow these steps in order:

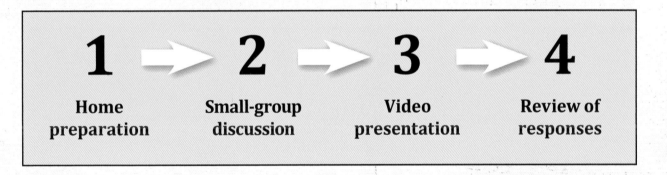

1	2	3	4
Home preparation	Small-group discussion	Video presentation	Review of responses

There are no responses for Session One.

The Annunciation – Luke 1:26-38

The Angel's Greeting (Luke 1:28)

1. Read **Luke 1:28**. *The angel's first word to Mary, "Hail" (Gk., chaire), literally means "rejoice." The command to rejoice evokes several notable occasions in the Old Testament, where it is used to address "Daughter Zion"—a biblical symbol for the faithful remnant of God's people.*

   a. *Consider the following prophecies, and record the reasons God's people will one day be called to "rejoice."*

   Zephaniah 3:14-15: Daughter Zion is called to rejoice because the LORD has taken away judgments against her; God has cast out Israel's enemies; the LORD is coming as King of Israel to dwell in the people's midst; and the people shall fear evil no more.

   Zechariah 9:9: Daughter Zion is called to rejoice because the King comes to Israel triumphant and victorious.

   b. *In light of this background, what do you think Gabriel's command to rejoice signals to Mary?*

   In light of these Old Testament prophetic calls to rejoice, Gabriel's words to Mary command a new Daughter of Zion to rejoice because the Lord is at last coming as King to Israel to rescue his people and save them from their enemies.

2. *Mary is not the first person to hear the assurance that, "The Lord is with you." This expression is frequently used by God (and his angels) to address someone who is called to an important mission.*

   a. *Read the following verses about the call of two Old Testament heroes, Moses and Gideon. Record the missions they are given, the obstacles or fears they face, and what God says in response. Then do the same for the verses related to Mary.*

Biblical Character	Mission	Obstacle/Fear	God's Assurance
Moses (Exodus 3:10-12)	Lead the people out of Egypt	Moses feels inadequate for the mission: "Who am I that I should go to Pharaoh, and bring the sons of Israel out of Egypt?" (verse 11)	I will be with you and will give you a sign.
Gideon (Judges 6:14-18)	Deliver Israel from the hand of Midian	Gideon also feels inadequate. He comes from a weak clan and wonders, "How can I deliver Israel?" (verse 15)	I will be with you and will give you a sign.

Biblical Character	Mission	Obstacle/Fear	God's Assurance
Mary (Luke 1:28-38)	Become the mother of a royal son (verses 32-36)	Mary is deeply troubled and asks, "How can this be, since I have no husband?" (verse 34)	The Lord will be with you (verse 28). "Do not be afraid, Mary, for you have found favor with God" (verse 30). You will conceive the child by the power of the Holy Spirit. Mary is also given a sign, the pregnancy of her aged cousin Elizabeth.

b. What similarities do you notice between these three scenes?

There are a number of similarities, including the following: Each involves someone given a great mission related to God's saving of Israel; each person has a specific fear; each person is assured that God will be with him or her; and each person is given a sign to help him or her to believe.

c. Given the way the assurance that "the Lord will be with you" is used by God and his angels in the Old Testament, what do you think Gabriel's words, "The Lord is with you," are meant to indicate to Mary even before the message is given?

The expression is used in the Bible to address people God calls to crucial tasks, those in which the future of Israel is at stake and for which the appointed people are incapable, on their own, of performing. Like Moses, Gideon, and other heroes in the Bible who are given a pivotal mission and assured that God will be with them, Mary, too, is being called to an important mission for which she will need to rely on God. The greeting indicates that God has in store for Mary a formidable task. But the angel assures her that she will not have to carry it out on her own. The Lord will be with her.

Mary's Initial Response (Luke 1:29)

3. *Read **Luke 1:29**. On hearing the angel's greeting, Luke tells us that Mary is "greatly troubled." Why do you think she responds this way?*

Some might say that the sight of an angel troubles Mary like Zechariah is troubled when the same angel appears to him in the Temple in the previous scene (Luke 1:11-12). But Luke's Gospel says that Mary is troubled not by the angel, but by his words, "[considering] in her mind what sort of greeting this might be." Mary might be awestruck at being called "full of grace" and being greeted with the word "hail," knowing what all that might mean. But most of all, when she hears the words, "the Lord is with you"—the same words spoken to the great leaders of Israel when they have been called to daunting missions—she may be "greatly troubled" at realizing that something big is about to be asked of her.

The Mission Revealed (Luke 1:30-37)

4. *The angel reveals Mary's mission in verse 31: "You will conceive in your womb and bear a son, and you shall call his name Jesus." Mary is to become a mother. But as the angel continues, he makes clear that the child she will bear will not be any ordinary child. Gabriel's words echo the famous promise God made to King David in 2 Samuel 7 to establish an everlasting dynasty through David's descendants.*

   a. *Read **2 Samuel 7:9-16**; then review **Luke 1:31-33**. Record the similar phrases in the box below.*

God's Promise to David 2 Samuel 7:9-16		Gabriel's Announcement to Mary Luke 1:32-33	
2 Samuel 7:9	"I will make for you a great name."	**Luke 1:32**	"He will be great."
2 Samuel 7:14	"I will be his father, and he shall be my son."	**Luke 1:32**	"[He] will be called the Son of the Most High."
2 Samuel 7:13	"I will establish the throne of his kingdom for ever."	**Luke 1:32**	"And the Lord God will give to him the throne of his father David."
2 Samuel 7:16	"And your house and your kingdom shall be made sure for ever."	**Luke 1:33**	"And he will reign over the house of Jacob for ever; and of his kingdom there will be no end."

   b. *How might these Old Testament Scripture passages shed light on what the angel Gabriel is telling Mary about the child she will bear?*

   God promises in 2 Samuel 7 that one day he will send a new son of David to restore the kingdom and extend its reign to the ends of the earth. The Jewish people in Jesus' day are longing for these prophecies about the Davidic kingdom to be fulfilled. So when Gabriel announces to Mary that she will have a child and describes him using royal images from the promises made to David (greatness, sonship, throne, house, everlasting kingdom), he is indicating that Mary's son will not be any ordinary child. He will be the long-awaited King, the son of David, who will restore the kingdom to Israel. The Jews refer to this anticipated royal Son as the *Messiah* (meaning, the "Anointed One").

5. *Read **Luke 1:34-35**. Awed by the angel's announcement, Mary wonders how it can be true—particularly because she is a virgin.*[1]

   a. *How does the angel respond to Mary's question?*

   The angel says that she will conceive by power of the Holy Spirit.

---

[1] Text note: The Revised Standard Version–Catholic Edition (RSV-CE) translates verse 34 as, "since I have no husband." However, the original Greek more literally reads, "since I do not know man." We have already seen that Mary's betrothal to Joseph means that they are legally married, but not yet living together. To "know a man" is a biblical euphemism for sexual relations. Hence, the New American Bible (NAB) translates this verse, "How can this be, since I have no relations with a man?"

b. Catechism *Connection:* Read *CCC 485 and 723*. What do these paragraphs add to your understanding?

Answers will vary. The Holy Spirit sanctifies the Virgin's womb and causes Mary "to conceive the eternal Son of the Father in a humanity drawn from her own" (CCC 485). In doing so, the Spirit fulfills God's loving plan.

6. Read *verses 36-37*. Here, the angel informs Mary of Elizabeth's miraculous pregnancy with John the Baptist. What details are given to Mary about Elizabeth's pregnancy, and how might they strengthen Mary's faith and provide reassurance?

The angel reminds Mary that her cousin—who is barren and of an age when childbearing is no longer possible—is in her sixth month of pregnancy. "For with God nothing will be impossible," he adds. It is worth pondering how this may encourage Mary and reinforce the credibility of her own, even more miraculous pregnancy. But there is something more. Not only does this information provide Mary with the encouragement of a similar miracle, it also gives her the support of a female relative at a potentially difficult time.

Mary, Servant of the Lord (Luke 1:38)

7. Read *verse 38*. In response to God's call in her life, Mary refers to herself as a "handmaid of the Lord." The word for handmaid (doule) *refers to a servant or slave.*

    a. Think about what it means to be a servant or slave. What does Mary's description of herself as a servant of the Lord and her response, "Let it be [done] to me according to your word," tell us about how she views her relationship with God?

    Mary sees herself as a servant of the Lord. Her life is not her own. She views her life as being completely at the disposal of God. She does not seek to use her life for her own purposes, but as a servant (slave) of God, she seeks to use her life to fulfill God's plans.

    b. Read Matthew 6:10. How does Mary's response in Luke 1:38 relate to the way Jesus teaches us to pray?

    Mary is a living example of the third petition of the Lord's Prayer: "Thy will be done." She is someone who truly lives this prayer by seeking to do God's will.

    c. Read Luke 22:42. How does Mary's response relate to Jesus' own example?

    Saying "yes" to God is not a one-time act. It must be renewed throughout our lives, especially in moments of suffering or times when God is challenging us to love more, to give more of ourselves to him or simply to trust him more. For example, Jesus, in the Garden of Gethsemane, feels the weight of all that is about to happen to him. But still he submits to this suffering, embracing his Father's will that he die for our sins. Mary's "yes" in Nazareth will lead her ultimately to the Cross, where she will have to renew that yes in a most profound and painful way as she watches her son die on Calvary.

"Blessed Among Women" (Luke 1:38-45)

1. Read **Luke 1:38-45.** *(If you are not familiar with the story of Elizabeth, also read **Luke 1:1-25.**)* *Why do you think Mary goes "with haste" (verse 39)? What might this reveal about her character?*

   The Bible does not tell us why Mary hurries to visit Elizabeth, but we can guess. She has astonishing news, and not many people will understand or be able to share her joy in the same way Elizabeth can. Mary believes the angel's message about Elizabeth's pregnancy, and she wants to help her (verse 56 tells us she remains with Elizabeth "about three months," which would be toward the end of Elizabeth's pregnancy). She also wants to share the good news of her own pregnancy. This demonstrates Mary's servant's heart and her trust in God's word to her. It also shows Mary's desire to share with Elizabeth her experience of a miraculous pregnancy and of being the mother of a child who is called by God to a special mission.

2. **a.** *In verse 42, Elizabeth says to Mary, "Blessed are you among women." Only two other women in the Bible are given this kind of praise: Jael and Judith. Read the following passages and note why they are called "blessed among women."*

   Judges 5:24-26 (Sisera was the general of the Canaanite army): Jael is immortalized in a song in which she is called blessed among women because she crushes the head of Sisera with a tent peg, thus delivering the people from their enemies.

   Judith 13:18 (The Assyrian general mentioned here is Holofernes): King Uzziah calls Judith blessed above all women when she cuts off the head of the leader of their enemies.

   b. **Think About It:** *Genesis 3:15, the first messianic prophecy in the Bible, stands in the background of this passage. In that text, God announces that "the woman's seed" will crush ("bruise" or "strike") the head of the serpent (which symbolizes the devil). Given this, why might Mary be associated with Jael and Judith? What do you think she has in common with these heroines of the Old Testament who also are described as "blessed among women"?*

   The image of "crushing" the head is used in the Bible from the very beginning of salvation history to describe God's defeat of the devil. From Genesis 3:15 on, God's people have been looking for someone to deal a death blow to the devil and his "seed," those who oppose the children of God. Jael and Judith play a role in God's plan of salvation by crushing the heads of those who participate in Satan's plots to oppress God's people. Like them, Mary plays a crucial role in God's salvation plan by giving birth to the child who will defeat the devil: On the Cross, Jesus will "crush the head of the serpent" and fulfill the prophecy of Genesis 3:15. Jael and Judith play a limited role in rescuing God's people from the oppression of their enemies; Mary will play a similar, but more crucial role, in God's ultimate plan to liberate humanity from sin and the devil.

3. *While God is often described as "LORD" or "the LORD" in the Old Testament, in verse 43, Elizabeth refers to Mary as "the mother of my Lord." Read* **2 Samuel 24:21.**

   a. *To whom is the expression "my Lord" addressed in this verse?*

   The expression "my Lord" is used in this passage to address King David.

   b. *In light of this background, what is Elizabeth saying about Mary when she addresses her as "the mother of my Lord"?*

   Elizabeth is saying that the child conceived in Mary's womb is the King and, therefore, that Mary is the mother of the King.

4. *The mother of the king played an important role in the Davidic kingdom in the Old Testament: that of the queen mother. In ancient near-eastern societies like the kingdom of Judah, the king often had many wives, some of whom had been given to him in marriage in the process of cementing political alliances with neighboring kingdoms. But each king had only one mother, and the queenship was given to her. Read the following passages, and note the ways in which the Bible depicts the authority of the mother of the king.*

   1 Kings 2:19-20: The queen mother is given a throne, where she is seated at the right hand of the king (a position of honor and authority). The king bows down before her and tells her that he will grant whatever she requests. This indicates the influential role the queen mother has as an advocate for the people.

   2 Kings 24:12: Here, the king's mother is listed as a member of the royal court along with the king's princes, servants, and palace officials.

   Proverbs 31:1-12: Proverbs 31 presents the queen mother's advice to her royal son, the king, about how to rule the kingdom with justice, taking care of the poor, avoiding too much drink, and choosing a good wife. The chapter indicates the influence the queen mother had as an important counselor to the king.

5. *"Hail Mary, full of grace, the Lord is with thee. Blessed art thou among women and blessed is the fruit of thy womb, Jesus"—The Hail Mary prayer begins with two sentences we see in our reading in Luke. The angel Gabriel greets Mary with the first prayer, and Elizabeth calls out the second as Mary approaches her. Write the rest of the prayer below. What connection do you see between the words of the Hail Mary and the role of the queen mother? (For further insight, read* **CCC 2676–2677.)**

   The Hail Mary continues as follows: "Holy Mary, Mother of God, pray for us sinners, now and at the hour of our death. Amen." Here, we seek Mary's intercession, asking her to pray for us—which is a fitting thing to do given the biblical perspective of her role as "Queen Mother." We have seen that as the mother of Jesus the King, Mary would be understood to be the "Queen Mother" in her son's kingdom. As Queen Mother, Mary would have the role of intercessor, bringing petitions from the citizens of the kingdom to her royal son, just like the queen mothers of the Old Testament once did. Therefore, we can approach Mary, our Queen Mother, with confidence, asking her to intercede with her son.

The Magnificat (Luke 1:46-55)

6. *Read **Luke 1:46-55**.*

   a. *In verses 46-49, who is the recipient of God's blessings, and how has this person been blessed?*

   In the first half of Mary's Magnificat, the focus is on what God has done for Mary, "his handmaiden." Mary has experienced God's saving hand in her life, indicated by her reference to God as "my Savior" (verse 47). Mary expresses how God has kindly looked upon her low estate (verse 48). She notes that God has done great things for her and that all generations will call her blessed (verses 48-49).

   b. *In the second half of Mary's prayer (verses 50-55), the focus changes. Who receives God's blessing in verses 50-55, and how?*

   The focus shifts in verse 50 from the individual, Mary, to "his servant Israel" (verse 54): God's people as a whole, who, like Mary, are the recipients of God's saving power. Mary praises God who has "exalted those of low degree" (verse 52) and who has "filled the hungry with good things" (verse 53), while he has come in judgment on the proud (verse 51), the mighty (verse 52), and the rich (verse 53). Indeed, God "has helped his servant Israel," remembering his promises to his people (verses 54-55).

   c. ***Think About It:*** *What do you think might be the connection between the first and second halves of Mary's prayer?*

   Answers will vary; encourage discussion. Mary stands as a representative of the people Israel. What God wants to do for Israel, he begins here to do for Mary. Just as God looks upon Mary's lowliness and exalts this young woman from Nazareth to become the mother of the Messiah, so God will mercifully look upon the poor, hungry, and lowly in all of Israel and rescue his people their enemies, their afflictions, and, most of all, their sins.

Mary as "Ark of the Covenant"

7. *In the Visitation scene, Luke's Gospel portrays Mary as making a journey that is similar to the one made by the Ark of the Covenant in 2 Samuel 6. The Ark of the Covenant in ancient Israel is the sacred vessel that carries the stone tablets of the Ten Commandments; the staff of Aaron, the first high priest; and a jar containing the manna from the desert. Most importantly, it is associated with the holy presence of God, which hovers over the Ark.*

   a. *Re-read **Luke 1:39-43, 56;** then read **2 Samuel 6:2, 9-16.** Answer these questions, noting the parallels between the two scenes. The first question has been done for you.*

2 Samuel 6:2, 9-16 **David and the Ark of the Covenant**	Luke 1:39-43, 56 **Mary on her way to see Elizabeth**
Where is the Ark of the Covenant? (verse 2) The Ark is in Baale-judah (which refers to the hill country of Judah).	*To where is Mary traveling? (verse 39)* Mary is going to a city in the hill country of Judea (Judah).
What question does David ask about the Ark? (verse 9) "How can the ark of the Lord come to me?	*What does Elizabeth ask about Mary? (verse 43)* "And why is this granted me, that the mother of my Lord should come to me?"
Where does the Ark stay? (verse 10) The house of Obed-edom	*Where does Mary stay? (verse 40)* The house of Zechariah
How long does the Ark stay there? (verse 11) Three months	*How long does Mary stay there? (verse 56)* Three months
How does David react to the LORD's presence in the Ark? (verse 16) David was leaping and dancing before the Lord.	*How does the baby in Elizabeth's womb react to the Lord's presence in Mary? (verse 41)* The babe leaped for joy.

b. *What do you think these parallels tell us about Mary? See also **CCC 2676**, under the subheading,* "Full of grace, the Lord is with thee."

Luke's incorporation of so much language from 2 Samuel 6 into his description strongly suggests he is trying to highlight a parallel between the Ark of the Covenant's journey to its resting point in Jerusalem ("the city of David") and Mary's journey to the home of Elizabeth where the presence of the promised Davidic King would first be acknowledged by another. Thus, the Bible reveals that Mary is like the Ark of the Covenant, "the dwelling place of God ... with men" (Revelation 21:3; CCC 2676). Like the Ark of the Covenant, Mary carries in her womb the presence of God. And just as the Ark carries the stone tablets of the Ten Commandments; the staff of Aaron, the high priest; and a jar containing the manna from the desert, so Mary carries Jesus, the one who fulfills the Law, who is the true High Priest and who is the bread of life. It is fitting, therefore, that in the Catholic Tradition Mary is known as the new Ark of the Covenant.

The Nativity – Luke 2:1-20

The Roman Census (Luke 2:1-7)

1. *Read **Luke 2:1-5**. Notice that Luke spends more time discussing the background circumstances than he spends on describing the details surrounding the birth of Jesus. In this way, Luke draws our attention to something in the historical context that he thinks is important to understanding the story of Christ's birth. What key word is used four times in these five verses?*

   Luke mentions the enrollment (or census) four times in these five verses.

2. *The Romans use a census to pay for their rule over the land. This particular census requires people to return to their ancestral hometowns. So Mary suddenly must travel with Joseph from Nazareth to Bethlehem, a journey of perhaps four or five days on foot, presumably in the last trimester of her pregnancy. Read **Luke 2:4-7** carefully, putting yourself in the place of Mary.*

   a. *What do you think Mary is going through as she journeys to Bethlehem for the census?*

   Answers will vary; encourage discussion. Participants may suggest that Mary experiences hardship in having to pick up and move in her last trimester, particularly because there were no comfortable cars available for the journey. The Bible does not say what means of travel they use, but most likely they walk. Whether on foot or by donkey, the trip cannot be comfortable for someone heavy with child.

   Others may consider Mary's thoughts of who this child she feels moving within her will be— particularly given her destination, which is repeated in four different ways by Luke in this section: "to Judea, to the city of David, which is called Bethlehem, because he was of the house and lineage of David" (verse 4). Surely she spends at least some time marveling over divine providence and the appropriateness of being moved there for the birth of the Christ child.

   b. *What do you think it is like for Mary to find "no place for them in the inn" and to deliver her child in these conditions? What emotions might she experience, and why?*

   Answers will vary. Mary probably experiences concern over where her child will be born and sorrow over the lack of room, over having to lay the child in a manger, over not being able to give her son the kind of warm environment fit for any newborn, let alone for Israel's Messiah King. She would also experience humility as her royal child is not welcomed. The birth of Israel's Messiah escapes the notice of all the leaders in Israel, and she has to give birth to Jesus in poor, humble conditions.

To Keep and Ponder (Luke 2:8-19)

3. *Jesus is born in humility and poverty; but in the region around Bethlehem, God's glory shines out and angels fill the sky, praising God and announcing the birth of the Savior to shepherds as they watch over their flocks. Read* **Luke 2:8-19** *carefully, focusing on* **verse 19.** *What is Mary's overall response to the events surrounding her son's birth—the trials, the poverty, and the humility of the Messiah's birth and the extraordinary testimony of the shepherds?*

In contrast to those who "wondered" (verse 18) and to the shepherds who went on their way rejoicing (verse 20), Mary kept all these things and pondered them in her heart (verse 19).

4. *Old Testament Connection: This idea of keeping and pondering in the heart is found several times in the Old Testament.*

a. *Read* **Genesis 37:5-11.** *What is the difference between the response of Joseph's brothers to his puzzling dream and the response of Joseph's father, Jacob (verse 11)?*

Joseph's brothers are jealous, but Joseph's father "kept the saying in mind." This points to how Joseph's father, while certainly puzzled by the dream, is still pondering its meaning, wanting to understand its message. Note that in the ancient Greek translation of the Old Testament known as the Septuagint, the word "kept" in **Genesis 37:11** is the same word used in Luke to describe how Mary "kept" all these things in her heart (Luke 2:19).

b. *Read* **Proverbs 3:1-2.** *What does the father in this proverb want his son to do?*

The father in this proverb exhorts his son not to forget his teaching, but rather to "let your heart keep my commandments." This will bring many years of blessing and welfare to his son. Again, this word "keep" is the same word used to describe Mary keeping and pondering in **Luke 2:19.**

c. *Read* **Psalm 119:11.** *What does the psalmist want to do with God's Word, and why?*

The psalmist praises God for his commandments and says he has laid up God's Word in his heart—like Mary keeping the mysterious events surrounding her son's birth in her heart. The psalmist goes on to say why: "That I might not sin against thee." In other words, the psalmist keeps God's Word in his heart, not just to memorize it or understand it intellectually, but so that he can live according to God's plan—so that he will not sin against God.

5. *Given the ways this idea of keeping and pondering is used in the Old Testament, what do you think it means for Mary to keep and ponder in her heart all that has happened in the events surrounding Jesus' birth?*

These Old Testament examples show that the idea of keeping and pondering something in one's heart describes a desire to understand the meaning of a mysterious event or divine message or teaching. As the examples from **Proverbs 3:1** and **Psalm 119:11** make clear, this desire for understanding is not just for intellectual purposes—it is also indicative of the person's desire to live according to God's teaching. Thus, Mary seeks to understand the mystery of her son's birth, both the humble and poor conditions in which Jesus is born and the glorious revelation about Jesus from the angels as announced by the shepherds. Mary wants to understand the mystery of her son's birth. (What does it mean? What does it say about her son and his mission?) She wants to understand so that she can live according to the mystery, allowing God's revelation to shape her life more deeply.

The Mysteries Surrounding Christ's Birth

6. *One aspect of the mystery surrounding Christ's birth is that Mary is forced by the Roman-decreed census to travel to Bethlehem. There is deep meaning in this move. Bethlehem is a city associated with royalty. It is the city from which King David came and a city that has taken on great importance for Israel's future hopes. Read* **Micah 5:2-4**[1] *(NAB 5:1-3) and answer the following questions.*

   a. *What does Micah's prophecy say will take place in Bethlehem?*

   Micah prophesies that from Bethlehem will come forth a ruler in Israel. Verses 3-4 indicate that a woman will bring forth a child who will be associated with the re-gathering of the exiled people of Israel. He will be a shepherd-like leader who will feed the flock of Israel and establish God's people "to the ends of the earth."

   b. *In light of this prophecy, how does God use the Roman census to serve a good purpose?*

   The Roman census provides the occasion for Mary and Joseph to move to Bethlehem so that this prophecy can be fulfilled.

7. *Another aspect of the mystery of Christ's birth is the angel's announcement of "good news ... to all the people," the birth of a Savior that causes the angelic hosts to proclaim peace on earth (Luke 2:10-14). In the first century, Caesar has been known as the "savior of the world" and as a "son of God," one who has brought "good news" of "peace" throughout the world. His birthday has been celebrated throughout the empire as the start of a new era.*

   Re-read **Luke 2:8-14.** *In light of this background, what does the angel's announcement tell us about Mary's child, and how do these verses of Luke's Gospel subvert the imperial propaganda regarding Caesar?*

   The angels announce that baby Jesus, not Caesar, is the true Lord, Son of God, and Savior of the world. It is Jesus' birth, not Caesar's, which brings the true Good News and peace to the world. It is Jesus' birth that will be remembered and celebrated throughout the world as the beginning of a new era. No one today celebrates the birth of Caesar Augustus. But millions around the world remember the birth of Jesus every Christmas.

8. *Luke makes a point of highlighting the humility, poverty, and rejection surrounding Christ's birth. This is a mystery that Mary will come to understand more profoundly years later, when her son is taken down from the Cross on Good Friday. Re-read* **Luke 2:7.** *Then read* **Luke 23:53** *and answer the following questions. Pay particular attention to the verbs that are used in both verses.*

   a. *What happens to Jesus' body when it is taken down from the Cross?*

   Jesus' body is wrapped in a linen shroud and laid in a rock-hewn tomb.

---

[1] Micah prophesied in the southern kingdom of Judah around the time the northern kingdom fell to Assyria and many of the people were taken into exile. He warned that a similar fate would befall Judah should they fail to repent and return to the Lord, while also foreseeing a day when a remnant of the exiles would be re-gathered and restored in Israel. It is this future return that these verses evoke.

b. *How is this similar to what happens to Jesus at his birth?*

Just as the baby Jesus is *wrapped* in swaddling clothes and *laid* in the manger, so will his body be *wrapped* in the linen shroud and *laid* in the tomb.

c. *In light of this literary connection, what might Luke be trying to tell us about God's Son?*

Israel's Messiah King, the Son of God, first manifests himself not in worldly glory, but in humility, poverty, suffering, and rejection. By making a verbal connection between Bethlehem and the Cross, Luke shows us that the humble way Jesus is born into this world foreshadows how he will leave this world at the climax of his mission, when he dies on the Cross. This is part of what Mary keeps and ponders in her heart and what she will come to understand more clearly over time, especially when she witnesses her son's death on Calvary.

9. **Catechism** *Connection: Mary, in her humble maternity, is the model for us all. Read* **CCC 563 and 725**. *What does this lesson mean for us as we seek to accept Jesus and bear his life into the world?*

Mary's meek acceptance of poor circumstances, poverty, and lack of acclaim for herself and her son models godly humility for us. We, too, must approach God by kneeling at a manger, adoring Christ in his weakness, accepting him with humility, and becoming humble as children. Paradoxically, there is strength in this as Pope Benedict XVI once explained: "The Son of God, through the work of the Holy Spirit, was incarnate in the womb of the Virgin Mary. This is an announcement that rings out ever new and in itself brings hope and joy to our hearts because, every time, it gives us the certainty that even though we often feel weak, poor and incapable in the face of the difficulties and evil in the world, God's power is always active and works miracles through weakness itself. His grace is our strength" (cf. 2 Corinthians 12:9-10).[2]

---

[2]   Benedict XVI, General Audience Address, January 2, 2013.

The Presentation & The Finding of Jesus in the Temple – Luke 2:21-52

Obedient Parents (Luke 2:21-24)

1. Read **Luke 2:21-24.** *In what ways are Mary and Joseph model and obedient Jewish parents?*

   Mary and Joseph do a number of things here that show them to be model and obedient Jews: They circumcise Jesus on the eighth day, as the Law requires (2:21); they name the child "Jesus," which Luke notes was "the name given by the angel" (1:31; 2:21); they go to Jerusalem for the purification "according to the law" (2:22); they present the child to the Lord in Jerusalem "as it is written in the law of the Lord" (2:23); and they offer the sacrifice "according to what is said in the law" (2:24).

2. *Verse 24 reports that Mary and Joseph bring a pair of turtledoves or two young pigeons for the purification ritual. Read what the Law requires in* **Leviticus 12:8.** *What does this tell us about the Holy Family?*

   Leviticus 12:6-8 describes the ceremony that was required for a mother's ritual purification after she delivered a child. The law normally required the sacrifice of one pigeon or turtledove and one, year-old lamb. However, if the woman could not afford a lamb, the law offered a more economical option: She could bring another bird instead. The fact that Mary brings the two birds and not a lamb indicates she is poor.

Simeon's Prophecy (Luke 2:25-35)

3. **Old Testament Connection:** *Read* **Luke 2:25-32,** *in which Simeon takes the child Jesus in his arms and utters a prophecy about the child's greatness, using words that recall a famous prophecy from the book of Isaiah.*

   a. *Now read that prophecy in* **Isaiah 42:1-6,** *which speaks about God's Servant, the Redeemer God will send to rescue Israel. What does God say he has done with this Servant? (See verse 6b.)*

   God has given the Servant "as a covenant to the people, a light to the nations."

   b. *Read* **Luke 2:32.** *What does Simeon say about Jesus in this verse that recalls* **Isaiah 42:6?**

   Simeon says that Jesus will be "a light for revelation to the Gentiles." (Facilitators may need to note that "Gentile" refers to the non-Israelite people, to all the other nations.)

   c. *What would this tell Mary about her child?*

   This prophecy of Simeon would signal to Mary and Joseph that their child is the fulfillment of Isaiah's prophecy about the Servant of the Lord who will redeem Israel and be a light to the nations. This would be a confirmation to Mary of what she learned from the angel Gabriel, that her son is the long-awaited Messiah.

4. *Next, Simeon utters a prophecy specifically to Mary. Read* **Luke 2:34-35.**

 a. *In verse 35, Simeon speaks of a sword. Read the following Old Testament passages and note what the image of the sword is used to describe.*

 Leviticus 26:6: The sword points here to war, to foreign nations overtaking the people. This verse says that the sword will *not* go through the land and thus there will be peace.

 Leviticus 26:7: Here the sword refers to Israel's victorious armies: Israel's enemies shall fall before its sword.

 Deuteronomy 32:25: Here the sword points to destruction coming upon young and old.

 b. *In light of this background, what does the image of the sword represent in the Old Testament? And what does this tell us about Simeon's prophecy about the child Jesus in* **Luke 2:33-35?**

 In the Old Testament, the image of the sword symbolized war, bloodshed, destruction, and death. Simeon's prophecy about the child indicates that Jesus will grow up and face not just opposition—being "a sign that is spoken against" (Luke 2:34)—but that he also will face the sword (Luke 2:35). The use of this word points to how he will be killed.

 c. *Now read* **John 19:31-35,** *the account of Jesus' death. How does Simeon's prophecy about the sword relate to Jesus' death on the Cross?*

 In Luke 2, Simeon prophesies about the child's future opposition and suffering. He associates the child Jesus with the image of the sword that will pierce Mary's soul also (see Luke 2:35). Simeon's prophecy can be seen as coming to fulfillment when the soldier pierces Jesus' side with a spear (see John 19:34).

 d. *Finally, what do you think Simeon's words about a sword piercing Mary's soul mean? Read also* **CCC 529.**

 These words point to the tremendous suffering Mary will experience in watching her son die on the Cross.

Lost in Jerusalem (Luke 2:41-45)

5. *Read* **Luke 2:41-45.** *It is easy to wonder today how Mary and Joseph could leave their son behind in the big city of Jerusalem. What do these verses tell us that might shed light on how these holy and responsible parents could lose their child so easily?*

 The pilgrims traveled to Jerusalem in large groups. Luke tells us that Mary and Joseph are "supposing him to be in the company" when they leave Jerusalem and that they assume Jesus is "among their kinsfolk and acquaintances" (verse 44). The facilitator may want to mention that it was common for extended family members to look after one's children on a journey like this. And while children generally would stay with the women, a boy of twelve, on the cusp of maturity, might also be among the men.

"My Father's House" (Luke 2:46-52)

6. *When Mary finally finds her son three days later, she asks why Jesus has treated his parents this way. But Jesus replies, "How is it that you sought me? Did you not know that I must be in my Father's house?" (Luke 2:49)*

    a. *What do you think it means that Jesus must be in his Father's house? See also* **CCC 534.**

    By "my Father's house," Jesus means not Joseph's house but the house of God, the Temple. Jesus draws a distinction between his loyalty to his earthly father and his loyalty to his heavenly Father. He will always honor his human parents, but his primary allegiance is to his heavenly Father's mission. As the *Catechism* explains, "Here Jesus lets us catch a glimpse of the mystery of his total consecration to a mission that flows from his divine sonship" (CCC 534). Jesus' desire to fulfill his heavenly Father's will may sometimes cause his human parents sorrow, as it has during these three days—and as it will in the future, especially when Mary witnesses Jesus dying on the Cross.

    b. *Read* **Luke 2:50.** *How well do Mary and Joseph understand these words of Jesus?*

    Mary and Joseph do not understand the meaning of Jesus' words.

    c. *Read* **Luke 2:51.** *What is Mary's response to this event? (See again CCC 534.)*

    Mary "kept all these things in her heart," pondering what they might mean. As the *Catechism* tells us, she may not understand the meaning of the words, but she accepts them in faith.

    d. *What might Mary's example teach us about how to respond when we do not understand why God allows us to experience moments of trial, uncertainty, or darkness or what God may be trying to teach us through these difficulties?*

    Mary does not yet understand fully why Jesus separates himself from her and what he means by saying he must be in his Father's house. But she continues to prayerfully keep all these things, pondering them in her heart—which, as we saw in the previous session, points to her desire to understand the mysteries unfolding before her so that she can conform her life to whatever the Lord is trying to teach her through them. In the same way, when we are faced with difficult or confusing situations, we should ponder them in prayer, asking God to help us understand what he is trying to teach us or the ways in which he is calling us to grow. We should trust as Mary does that no matter what crosses we may face in life, God can always bring about some good in our soul through them.

7. *This experience of Mary and Jesus anticipates what will happen to them at the climax of his mission. Answer the questions in the following chart, noting how this scene from Luke 2 might prefigure the events surrounding Jesus at the culmination of his public ministry and Mary's involvement there.*

Twelve-year-old Jesus lost in the Temple (Luke 2:41-52)	Jesus approaching the culmination of his public ministry
Read Luke 2:41. *Jesus travels from Galilee to what city?* Jerusalem	**Read Luke 9:51.** *Near the end of his public ministry, Jesus travels from Galilee to what city?* Jerusalem
Read Luke 2:41. *For what feast does Jesus travel to this city?* Passover	**Read Luke 22:1.** *What feast is approaching when Jesus arrives in the city?* Passover
Read Luke 2:46. *What building does Jesus visit there?* The Temple	**Read Luke 19:45.** *What building does Jesus visit there?* The Temple
Read Luke 2:45. *What happens between Mary and Jesus while he is in this city?* They are separated from each other.	**Think About It:** *What happens between Mary and Jesus on Good Friday when Jesus is crucified?* They are separated from each other by death.
Read Luke 2:46. *On what day of the week are Mary and Jesus reunited?* On the third day	**Read Luke 9:22.** *On what day after his death would Mary and Jesus have been reunited?* On the third day

The Wedding at Cana – John 2:1-11

Understanding the Context (John 1:1–2:1)

1. *John's Gospel begins with many images from the story of Creation in Genesis 1. Read* **John 1:1-5.** *What are some of the ways these verses recall the story of Creation?*

    Facilitators: Invite participants to share the reflections they discovered, which may include some of the following: "In the beginning ..." (John 1:1) is a quote from Genesis 1:1: "In the beginning God created the heavens and the earth." "All things were made through him" (John 1:3) recalls God's creation of the universe. "Life" (John 1:4) brings to mind the life—plants, animals, birds, fish, man and woman—God created. "Light" (John 1:4) recalls God creating light on the first day. "The light shines in the darkness" (John 1:5) brings to mind how God separated the light from the darkness in Genesis 1:3.

2. **a.** *The Creation theme continues as John narrates a series of days that together make up a new Creation week.* **John 1:19** *is the first day in the narrative that reports the testimony of John the Baptist. Read that and then read about the others, which are listed in order below. For each one, record what happens and when the Gospel says the event takes place.*

    John 1:29: John the Baptist first calls Jesus "the Lamb of God" on "the next day" after the priests and Levites question him.

    John 1:35-36: John the Baptist again calls Jesus "the Lamb of God" on "the next day" following the time recorded in 1:29.

    John 1:43: Jesus decides to go to Galilee on "the next day" after he calls, "Behold, the Lamb of God!" in verse 36.

    John 2:1: The wedding at Cana takes place "on the third day" after Jesus decides to go to Galilee.

    b. *Review your responses to 2.a. and count through the days until you reach the wedding at Cana. On what day in John's narration is the wedding?* Participants may use the box on page 49 to help them calculate. They can then record their answers in the blank space at the bottom of the box.

	John 1:19	John 1:29	John 1:35	John 1:43	John 2:1
John's Chronological Markers	Start of John's narrative	"The next day"	"The next day"	"The next day"	"On the third day"
Day Number	Day 1	Day 2	Day 3	Day 4	Day 7
Explanation	1	1+1= _2_	2+1= _3_	3+1= _4_	4+3= _7_

The wedding feast at Cana takes place on the <u>seventh</u> day.

3. ***Think About It:*** *Given the symbolism of the Creation story that you have seen in John's Gospel, what might John be pointing out with this symbolism involving the number of days?*

The wedding at Cana takes place on the seventh day, at the climax of a series of days that John's Gospel delineates. This continues the Creation themes started in John 1:1-5. Just as the story of Creation begins with seven days, so does the story of Jesus in John's Gospel begin with seven days that symbolize how Jesus is coming to renew creation.

No Wine, but Much Faith (John 2:1-3)

4. *Read **John 2:1-3,** in which Mary brings the shortage of wine to Jesus' attention.*

a. *At this point in the Gospel, Jesus has yet to perform any miracles. What might this tell us about Mary's faith in her son? See also **John 20:29.***

Even though Jesus has yet to perform any miracles, Mary believes he can miraculously provide wine in this time of need. She thus exhibits the faith Jesus praises when he says, "Blessed are those who have not seen and yet believe" (John 20:29).

b. *What might Mary's example teach us?*

Answers will vary; encourage discussion. While seeking human solutions to our problems is prudent, we should follow Mary's example and turn our troubles over to Jesus. She brings the problem to her son, simply stating it without elaborating or telling him how to solve the problem. We, like Mary, should instinctively turn to Jesus with our daily trials and troubles, trusting that he will help us and guide our lives.

The Woman (John 2:4-10)

5. *Read **John 2:4.** How does Jesus reply to Mary's request, and what do you think of his reply?*

Jesus answers Mary, "O woman, what have you to do with me? [or, as it also can be translated, "What is that to you and me?"]. My hour has not yet come." He uses the impersonal "woman" instead of "Mother." For some people, this might sound cold or harsh, as if Jesus is trying to rebuff her.

6. *Now read **John 2:5**. How does this verse suggest that Mary interprets Jesus' words?*

The context makes clear that whatever these words mean, they should not be interpreted in a negative light. As verse 5 indicates, Mary seems to assume Jesus will do something about the problem she brings to his attention. If she did not believe that he would act in the situation, she would not direct the servants to help him.

7. *Read **John 2:6-10**. Do these verses seem to indicate that Jesus is refusing Mary's request or responding positively to her petition? Explain.*

Jesus does not respond negatively, but responds to her request by solving the problem.

Note: Similar language is used in John 19:26, where Jesus calls Mary "woman" from the Cross. There, he is lovingly providing for her, not being disrespectful at all. Some people find Jesus' words in verse 4 dismissive (including, "What have you to do with me? My hour has not yet come"). These expressions will be addressed in the video.

8. **Old Testament Connection:** *Read **Genesis 3:14-15**. These verses represent the first messianic prophecy in the Bible. In light of Genesis 3:15, what is Jesus saying about himself and about his mother when he calls her "woman"? Read also **CCC 410–411**.*

By calling his mother "woman" in the context of allusions to the Genesis account of Creation, Jesus recalls the prophecy that "the woman" and "her seed" (her offspring) will have the final victory over the devil (Genesis 3:14-15). Here at Cana stands "the woman"—Mary, the "new Eve," whose "seed," Jesus, will crush the head of the devil whom the serpent symbolizes.

"Do Whatever He Tells You" (John 2:5-11)

9. *Confident that her son will answer her request, Mary says to the servants, "Do whatever he tells you" (verse 5). These words recall a theme of obedience in the Old Testament and offer rich insight into how we are called to be obedient.*

a. *Read the following passages in which the people of Israel make or renew their covenant with God after having heard the Word of the LORD spoken to them. Note what the people say they will do in response to what God says.*

Exodus 19:8: "All that the LORD has spoken we will do."

Joshua 24:24: "The LORD our God we will serve, and his voice we will obey."

Nehemiah 5:12: "We will do as you say."

b. *How do you think this Old Testament background sheds light on Mary's instruction to the servants to "do whatever he tells you"?*

Mary instructs the servants to give the proper response to God's Word, which is to do whatever God says.

c. *How might Mary's instruction inspire you to follow God's Word more closely in your life?*

Mary's words, "Do whatever he tells you," echo through the ages, challenging Christians to faithful obedience. This includes following Jesus' teachings as handed down through the Church and also includes being faithful to the small ways Christ may prompt us to be more like him. For example, Christ may prompt us to be more generous, patient, pure, forgiving, or kind. When we sense the Spirit knocking on the door of our hearts, inviting us to be more like Christ, we should follow Mary's exhortation: "Do whatever he tells you."

10. *Nearby stand six stone jars, the kind used to hold water for the ceremonial washing required before a meal. Each would be large enough to hold twenty to thirty gallons of water, but they are apparently empty—possibly the water has already been used by the guests at the wedding.*

    a. *For each verse below, note what Jesus commands and how the servants respond.*

      John 2:7: Jesus commands them, "Fill the jars with water." The servants "filled them up to the brim."

      John 2:8: Jesus says, "Now draw some out, and take it to the steward of the feast." We read that they responded in obedience and "took it."

    b. *How faithful do you think the servants are in responding to Jesus' commands? Explain.*

      The servants respond like model disciples. They promptly and perfectly obey Jesus' commands, filling the jars with water (even to the brim) and taking the wine to the steward of the feast—just as Jesus instructs.

    c. *What might the servants' exemplary response tell us about the impact of Mary's exhortation in this scene?*

      Mary's command, "Do whatever he tells you," has a tremendous impact, inspiring the servants to respond obediently to Jesus like faithful disciples.

11. *When the steward tastes the water, it has miraculously become fine wine. Read* **John 2:11.**

    a. *What does this verse tell us about the significance of Jesus' action at the wedding feast?*

      This is the first of Jesus' signs—a reference in John's Gospel to his miracles. This is the first time Jesus reveals his glory and the first time the disciples as a group come to believe in Jesus. It is the first miracle and marks the launch of Jesus' public ministry.

    b. *What might this verse tell us about the role and importance of Mary in Jesus' public ministry?*

      Mary plays an important role in this scene, setting in motion Jesus' first miracle. Her initial intercession, presenting the wine shortage problem to Jesus, provides the occasion for Jesus to perform his first miracle. Her command to the servants to "do whatever he tells you" inspires them to obey Christ's instructions so that the wine can be provided.

Standing at the Cross of Jesus (John 19:25)

1. *Mary only appears twice in John's Gospel. She is first mentioned in conjunction with Jesus' miracle at the wedding at Cana: "the first of his signs," in which he reveals his glory publicly for the first time and when his disciples come to believe in him. This is the start of Jesus' public ministry. The next occasion is in **John 19:25-30,** where she appears at Jesus' death on the Cross. **Think About It:** What is significant about the fact that John records her presence at just these two events?*

   Though Mary only appears twice in John's Gospel, she appears at crucial moments in Christ's mission: at the start of his public ministry, when he performs his first miracle and reveals his glory at Cana, and at the climax of his public ministry, when he dies on the Cross for our sins. This highlights the importance of her role in his life and mission.

2. **a.** *Read the following verses and answer the questions to better understand Mary's role as she stands at the foot of the cross of Jesus.*

   Matthew 16:21: *What does Jesus say will happen to him in Jerusalem?*

   Jesus tells his disciples he must be handed over to the Jewish leaders, be killed, and be raised on the third day.

   Matthew 16:24: *What does Jesus say his disciples must do?*

   Jesus tells the disciples that they must deny themselves, take up their crosses, and follow him.

   John 16:32: *What does Jesus predict the apostles will do in the hour of his passion?*

   Jesus predicts that the apostles will scatter and leave him alone when he is arrested and crucified.

   Matthew 26:56: *What do the disciples do when Jesus is arrested in the Garden of Gethsemane?*

   They all run away (doing what Jesus has predicted they will do).

   John 19:25: *What are Mary and the other women doing in this verse?*

   Mary and the other women are described as "standing by the cross of Jesus."

   b. *What might this tell us about Mary?*

   Mary is a model, faithful disciple, following Jesus to the Cross, while most of the other disciples abandon him. She shares in his self-emptying and pain, perhaps recalling Simeon's prophecy that "a sword will pierce through your own soul also" (Luke 2:35). Mary is not afraid as the other disciples seem to be; she may grieve with him, but her "perfect love" for her son is such that it "casts out fear" (see 1 John 4:18).

c. *Think back over the things you have learned about Mary so far. What might be going through Mary's mind as she stands there watching Jesus die? And what might give her the strength and grace needed to be the exemplary disciple who follows him to the Cross?*

The Bible does not reveal Mary's thoughts at this scene. But considering what Scripture tells us about Mary, we might imagine that she recalls the joyous messages of the angel and Elizabeth about her child being the Messiah. She might recall Jesus' poverty and humiliation at the Nativity, Simeon's words about the sword at the Presentation, and Jesus' own words about being in his "Father's house" when he was lost and found in the Temple.

Mary may wonder how this crucified one can be the King? (As St. John Paul II once noted, Jesus' death on the Cross seems to be the complete negation of all that Gabriel revealed to Mary about her son's kingship.) All Mary has to rely on for support is her faith: in her son and in what God has revealed to her during the course of his life. These events foreshadow her suffering at the foot of the Cross. Her total trust in God's words to her through the angel Gabriel and what she has learned about her son during his childhood probably help carry her through this climactic moment on Calvary in great faith.

3. *In **John 16:20-22**, Jesus uses the analogy of a woman giving birth to help the disciples understand that although they will experience sorrow at his suffering and death, the sorrow will turn to joy when they are reunited with him in his resurrection. Read **John 19:25-27** together with **John 16:20-22**, looking for similar words and themes. How does John describe Mary at the Cross in ways that recall the allegory of the woman in labor—revealing her as a model, faithful disciple participating in Christ's passion?*

Both passages use the key words "woman" and "hour," and both passages involve the themes of motherhood and the suffering that Jesus' followers experience. First, we will address the key words: "woman" and "hour." The mother in the birth allegory is called a "woman" in travail who gives birth when her "hour" has come (16:21). At the Cross, Mary is called "woman," and from "that hour" the Beloved Disciple takes her to his home (19:26-27). Second, we will consider the thematic links of motherhood and suffering. The woman in John 16 is a *mother* giving birth to her son, and her labor pains symbolize the *suffering* Christ's followers will face when he is crucified. Motherhood and suffering also play an important role in the scene with Mary at the Cross. She is introduced as the *mother* of Jesus (19:25) and there becomes the *mother* of the Beloved Disciple—"Behold, your mother!" (19:27). And this takes place at Jesus' crucifixion when his disciples experience great *suffering* over his death.

Mary and the Beloved Disciple

4. *Read **John 19:25-27**. What might Jesus' entrusting of his mother to his Beloved Disciple's care tell us about the relationship Jesus has with Mary?*

One of Jesus' last acts is to entrust Mary to the Beloved Disciple (John). This shows his tremendous filial love and piety as he considers his mother's needs in his dying moments.

5. *Let us now consider how this action might also point to a profound spiritual reality.*

a. *John's Gospel often uses individual characters to represent larger groups. For example, the Samaritan woman at the well is also seen as a representative of all Samaritans who will come to* *believe in Jesus. And Nicodemus, the Pharisee in John 3, represents all the Pharisees who will fail to understand Jesus and instead will oppose him. Similarly, the "Beloved Disciple" is traditionally recognized as the apostle John, but in the fourth Gospel, he also represents a larger group of people. Read the following verses in which the Beloved Disciple appears, and record what John's Gospel says about him.*

John 13:25: John is "close to the breast of Jesus" at the Last Supper.

John 19:26: John is at the Cross with Jesus (the only apostle to remain with Jesus at his crucifixion).

John 20:8: John is first to believe in the risen Christ.

John 21:7: John bears witness to the risen Christ.

b. *What does this tell us about those the Beloved Disciple might represent?*

As the one disciple who is closest to Jesus at the Last Supper, the one who remains with him at the Cross while the others abandon him, the one who first believes in Christ's resurrection, and the one who tells others about it, the Beloved Disciple stands out as *the* exemplary disciple who represents all faithful followers of Christ.

c. *Now read **John 19:26-27** again. Mary has been looking on as her only son dies before her eyes. What does he say to her and to the Beloved Disciple?*

Jesus says, "Woman, behold, your son!"—not referring to himself, but redirecting her attention to the Beloved Disciple standing beside her.

d. *Considering what you learned in 5.a. and 5.b., how do these words expand the relationship between Jesus and Mary into something far greater? See also **CCC 501 and 2674.***

Mary can be seen as the spiritual mother of all Jesus' faithful disciples, whom the Beloved Disciple represents.

The Woman and the Hour

6. *Mary's important role in God's plan of salvation also can be seen in light of the theme of "the hour" in John's Gospel. The hour of Jesus, first mentioned at the wedding at Cana when Jesus says his "hour has not yet come," reaches its climax in his passion.*

a. *Read the following verses and note what "the hour" describes.*

John 5:25-28: The hour is associated with the Last Judgment and eternal life.

John 7:30: The hour is associated with Jesus' arrest. The Pharisees try to arrest him, but his hour has not yet come.

John 12:23-24: The hour is the hour of Jesus' glorification; but this glory involves dying in order to bear much fruit, like a grain of wheat that falls to the earth and dies.

John 12:27, 31-33: These verses continue to describe what will happen in Christ's hour: The ruler of this world will be cast out, and Jesus will draw all men to himself. Finally, John's Gospel reveals that this hour is ultimately associated with Jesus' death.

b. *Now review **Genesis 3:15**. What is the relationship between this prophecy and Jesus' hour as described in **John 12:31**?*

John 12:31 reveals that the hour of Jesus is the hour when "the ruler of this world will be cast out"—in other words, the hour when the devil is defeated and Genesis 3:15 is fulfilled. This is the hour when the woman's son crushes the head of the serpent as Genesis 3:15 foretold.

c. *In light of this theme of the hour, what do you think is the meaning of Jesus calling his mother "woman" in the "hour" of his passion? See also **CCC 2618**.*

Jesus calling Mary "woman" within this scene, which has Genesis 3:15 in the background, points to Mary as the "woman" of Genesis 3:15—the woman who will have the son who will defeat the devil. As the *Catechism* says, "It is at the hour of the New Covenant, at the foot of the cross,[1] that Mary is heard as the Woman, the new Eve, the true 'Mother of all the living'" (CCC 2618).

7. **Old Testament Connection:** *The book of 2 Maccabees recalls the forced Hellenization of Jews in Palestine under the Greek ruler Antiochus Epiphanes. The resulting persecution led to courageous resistance by many of the faithful. Read **2 Maccabees 7:1-39**. In what ways might the mother in this story prefigure Mary at the Cross?*

The mother in this passage witnesses the killing of her sons by a Gentile ruler, like Mary witnesses the crucifixion of her son at the hands of the Romans. The mother totally entrusts her sons into the care of God and encourages her sons to remain faithful. She has faith that her children will be raised and that she will be reunited with them (verses 14, 29). Her faith prefigures Mary's great faith in God's plan and her hope for her son's resurrection.

[1] Cf. John 19:25-27.

Mary Crowned with Glory – Revelation 12

The Woman and Her Child (Revelation 12:1-5)

1. *Read **verses 1-4** again and describe the "portents" or "signs"[1] John sees in heaven.*

   John sees a woman in the throes of birth pangs, who is "clothed with the sun, with the moon under her feet, and on her head a crown of twelve stars" (12:1). He also sees "a great red dragon" (12:3) that tries to devour the son she is about to bear (12:4).

2. *Who is this woman? One key to understanding this is to consider the identity of the child to whom she gives birth.*

   a. *What does verse 5 tell us about the woman's child?*

   The child is taken up to a throne and will rule all nations with a rod of iron.

   b. *Read **Psalm 2:9,** a prophetic text about the LORD's anointed King, the Messiah. What does this verse tell us about the future Messiah?*

   The Messiah will rule all nations with a rod of iron.

   c. *In light of this background, who do you think the child is?*

   The child is the Messiah, Jesus—the one who is taken up to a throne in heaven and the one whom Psalm 2:9 foretold would rule all nations with a rod of iron.

3. *If this is true about the child, then who might the woman who gives birth to him be?*

   At a most basic level, Christians should see the woman as Mary since she is the mother of the Messiah. This does not rule out other symbolic interpretations (such as the woman representing Israel giving birth to the Messiah or the woman symbolizing the Church giving life to its members, the faithful Christians). But it is very unlikely that Christians in the first century would have read about the mother of the Messiah and not thought at all about the mother of Jesus, Mary.

The Woman and the Dragon (Revelation 12:5-12)

4. *Let us now consider how this woman is depicted here as the new Eve.*

   a. *Review **Genesis 3:15.** What does God say will happen between the woman described there and the serpent (a symbol for the devil)?*

   The woman will have a child ("seed") who will crush the head of the serpent.

---

[1] A sign in the Bible is "an act, event, or object that points beyond itself to something else, often a greater or unseen reality. Signs can serve to impart a message or key image, to give a reminder or memorial, to give an omen or portent, or to display the loving and powerful work of God" (*Catholic Bible Dictionary*, Scott Hahn, General Editor).

b. Now read **Revelation 12:5-9.** *What happens to the dragon when the woman's male child is born?*

The dragon tries to attack the male child, but the child is caught up to God and to his throne. A war breaks out, and Michael and his angels defeat the dragon by throwing him out of heaven and down to earth.

c. *According to **Revelation 12:9,** who is the dragon?*

The dragon is "that ancient serpent,"—the serpent of Genesis 3:15, Satan, deceiver of the world.

d. *If the dragon in Revelation 12 is the serpent of **Genesis 3:15** at the moment of his defeat, who would the "woman" be in light of this Genesis 3:15 background?*

In light of this background, the woman of Revelation 12 (Mary) should be seen as the woman of Genesis 3:15—the woman whose child brings about the defeat of the serpent. In other words, the woman of Revelation 12 is the new Eve.

The Woman and Her Other Offspring (Revelation 12:13-17)

5. *Read **Revelation 12:17.***

a. *According to this verse, the woman has other offspring. How are these other offspring described?*

Her "other offspring" are described as "those who keep the commandments of God and bear testimony to Jesus" (verse 17).

b. *In the vision in this verse, who are the "other offspring" on earth?*

The woman's other offspring are those faithful disciples of Jesus, the Christians who keep God's commandments and bear witness to Christ.

c. *Considering that the woman represents Mary, what does that suggest about Mary's relationship with us? Read also **CCC 501.***

This suggests that Mary, who only had one physical child while on earth, has "other," spiritual, offspring who are the faithful disciples of her son, the firstborn of many. In that sense, Mary is the mother of all Christians. She is "the woman" who is the mother of those who keep the commandments of God and bear testimony to Jesus.

The Crown of Twelve Stars

6. *According to Revelation 12:1, the woman is depicted as having a crown of twelve stars on her head. Read **2 Timothy 4:7-8,** in which another heavenly crown is described.*

a. *Because of what qualities does Paul say he and others will receive "the crown of righteousness" in heaven?*

Paul says he will be awarded the crown of righteousness based on his perseverance in faith—his faithfulness to Christ—all throughout his life. He has fought the good fight. He has finished the race. He has kept the faith. He thus trusts that he will receive his reward, his crown of righteousness, in heaven.

b. *What would this tell us about Mary, who wears a crown in Revelation 12:1?*

Mary should be understood as someone who perseveres in faith as well. She, too, has been rewarded the crown of righteousness.

7. *Read the following passages, noting how Mary is depicted in the Bible as a persevering, faithful disciple throughout her life—and thus someone worthy of "the crown of righteousness."*

Luke 1:38: Mary describes herself as the handmaid of the Lord and says she will do what the Lord wants.

Luke 1:39: Mary goes in haste to visit Elizabeth, trusting the angel's message about Elizabeth's miraculous pregnancy.

Luke 1:45: Mary is described as blessed for having believed in the angel's announcement to her.

Luke 2:19: At the mystery of her son's birth, Mary keeps all these things and ponders them in her heart.

Luke 2:51: In response to Jesus' mysterious words about being in his Father's house, Mary keeps all these things and ponders them in her heart.

John 19:25-27: Unlike most of the other disciples, Mary remains standing by the cross of Jesus.

Acts 1:14: After Jesus' ascension, Mary remains in Jerusalem praying with the disciples before Pentecost.

8. *What aspects of Mary's example of faith from the verses above inspire you the most in your own faith to pursue the crown of righteousness that awaits all Christians?*

This question is open-ended. One might be moved by, Mary's belief in the angel's words, by her viewing herself as a servant of the Lord, by her pondering in her heart the mysteries unfolding before her, or by her trusting and surrendering at the Cross.

St. John Paul II on Mary's Assumption

"Today the liturgy invites us to contemplate Mary, taken up body and soul into heaven. By a special privilege, she was enriched by divine grace from the moment of her conception, and Christ, who ascended to the right hand of the Father, opened the doors of his kingdom to her, first among human creatures. Now from heaven, where the Queen of the angels and saints is crowned, the Mother of God and of the Church is close to the Christian people before whom she shines as the "new and immaculate woman (who) mediated for the guilt of the first woman."[2]

– St. John Paul II, The Angelus, August 15, 1999

[2] *Sacramentarium Gregorianum, Praefatio in Assumpt.*, n. 1688.

Then ...
Dive into Scripture with
The Great Adventure Foundational Series

Step 1
**The Bible Timeline:
The Story of Salvation**

Step 2
**Matthew:
The King and His Kingdom**

Step 3
**Acts:
The Spread of the Kingdom**

Continue the Journey

Exodus   Psalms   The Prophets   First Corinthians   Galatians   James   Revelation

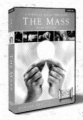

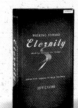

Mary   The Mass   Life Application

Catholic Bible Study Resources

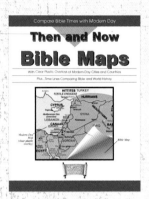

Then and Now Maps

The clear plastic overlays on these full-color maps allow you to compare the places mentioned in the Bible with modern-day cities.

20 pages - spiral bound - 8 ½ x 11

The Bible Thumper; Volumes. 1 & 2

A mini-concordance Bible verse finder with more than 1,000 easy-to-access verses to help Catholics locate and explain the basic teachings of the Faith. Each volume folds out to 33 inches and fits inside most Bibles.

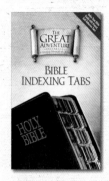

Great Adventure Catholic Bible Indexing Tabs

These pre-cut, one-inch, self-adhesive tabs fit the pages of any full-size Bible and are a great way to help you quickly locate each book of the Bible.

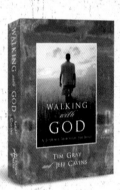

Walking With God: A Journey Through the Bible

by Tim Gray and Jeff Cavins

This captivating and inspirational book follows the central story woven throughout Scripture to reveal God's glorious plan of salvation.

296 pages

The Bible Compass: A Catholic's Guide to Navigating the Scriptures

by Edward Sri

Get the tools to study the Word of God with confidence, purpose, and in the appropriate context. This book demonstrates how to read the Bible within the living Tradition of the Catholic Church and addresses a host of common questions about the Bible.

174 pages

The Bible Timeline Guided Journal

by Sarah Christmyer

This is more than just a journal; it is a personal guide through the story of salvation history that will help you read the fourteen narrative books of the Bible. The journal includes room for notes as well as thought-provoking questions and tips on how to study the Bible.

236 pages

Praying Scripture for a Change: An Introduction to Lectio Divina

by Tim Gray

If you are looking for a way to get the most out of prayer, this book is indispensable. Theologian and biblical scholar Dr. Tim Gray walks you through the Bible and teaches you the simple steps of *lectio divina*, a practical and effective way to enhance your prayer life.

Book, 144 pages
Study Guide, 32 pages